The
Changing Face of
EXMOOR

Edited by
Hilary Binding

EXMOOR
BOOKS

First Published in 1995 by Exmoor Books

Copyright © 1995
Allan Straw,
Heather Wilson,
Edward Maltby,
Vanessa Straker and Keith Crabtree,
Veryan Heal,
Hilary Binding,
Stephen Essex,
Andrew R. Harrison and Richard Dunn,
Mark Blacksell,
Rachel Thomas.

ISBN 0 86183 282 5

British Library Cataloguing-in Publication Data
CIP data for this book is available from the British Library

EXMOOR BOOKS
Official publisher to the Exmoor National Park Authority

Halsgrove House
Lower Moor Way
Tiverton
EX16 6SS

Telephone 01884 243242
Facsimile 01884 243325

Printed by Longdunn Press Ltd., Bristol.

CONTENTS

Record of the Proceedings of a Geographical Symposium held on 24 September 1994 to discuss the changing face of Exmoor, current research and the challenge for the future

Jointly organised by
The Exmoor National Park Authority and
The Royal Geographical Society (South West Region).

This book is dedicated to Dr Leonard Curtis
(University of Bristol; National Park Officer 1978-88)
who pioneered research into soils on Exmoor
and inspired many of the contributors.

The financial support given by the **South Western Electricity Board**
and the **Nationwide Building Society** is gratefully acknowledged.

FOREWORD

Exmoor's wild yet intimate scenery, composed of open moorland interspersed with ancient walled and hedgerowed hill farms and browsed by sheep and deer, that folds into sheltered combes, flanked by verdant deciduous woodland and majestic cliffs that drop to the Bristol Channel, has inspired some of England's most renowned authors and poets. It has also been a delight to Westcountrymen and visitors alike. As leisure time increases even more people will be coming to enjoy its beauties through varying recreational pursuits which, together with the interests of landholders, have to be balanced in such a way that freedom of access does not in any way impair Exmoor's incomparable assets for enjoyment by future generations. The conservation of the moor and its environs has fortunately been at the forefront of national and local policies for many years and led to its designation as a National Park in 1954.

On this fortieth anniversary it was thought appropriate that the Royal Geographical Society, through its South West Region, should come together with the Exmoor National Park Authority to hold a weekend symposium and field trip to review the changing face of Exmoor. This was particularly apposite as there is no major geographical memoir on Exmoor as a whole and much of archaeological note has yet to be investigated. A number of geographical research projects are in progress and it seemed a good opportunity to present an overview of current research together with a summary of the present state of knowledge of Exmoor's geomorphological and ecological antecedents. The event comprised a full day seminar on Saturday, 24 September 1994 and a choice of two field trips the next day; one in the heart of the moor and one on the coast and fringing woodlands.

This publication brings together the papers that were presented at the seminar. The organising committee was particularly pleased to be able to assemble, as speakers or chairpersons, academics and researchers, people concerned with Exmoor from all three major Universities of the South West; Bristol, Exeter and Plymouth, as well as from London and Cambridge Universities, Exmoor National Park itself and the Countryside Commission.

The paper by Professor Allan Straw of the University of Exeter introduces the geomorphology of the moor, while his former colleague, Dr Edward Maltby, who had recently been appointed Professor of Environmental and Physical Geography at the University of London, describes ecological change on the moor with special reference to its soils. The coastal geomorphology is described in the paper by Heather Wilson, Deputy Warden of the Leonard Wills Field Centre at Nettlecombe, who has been leading field trips on this coast for over twenty years, while the paper by Dr Stephen Essex of the University of Plymouth reviews the role of the Park in woodland conservation and management. The Park's own archaeologist, Veryan Heal, gives an overview of the archaeology of the Moor, while Vanessa Straker of the University of Bristol describes her ongoing paleoenvironmental research on Exmoor. Hilary Binding, an educational consultant and the editor of this publication, discusses in her paper more recent historical change on Exmoor and the ebb and flow of agriculture and other developments related to changing economic circumstances. The paper by Dr Andrew Harrison of Bristol University draws all these earlier physical, archaeological and historical presentations together in describing their effects on the changing landscapes of Exmoor, and his research studies on behalf of the National Park in this sphere. Finally Professor Mark Blacksell, who last year moved from the Exeter Geography Department to take the chair at the University of Plymouth, draws all the day's threads together into a paper which traces the major aspects of change over the past four decades and evaluates their impact on, and contribution to, Exmoor's National Park status.

Our thanks go to all the speakers (and in two cases their colleagues who collaborated with them) whose papers are presented here. Thanks also go to Professor Richard Chorley, the eminent geomorphologist from the University of Cambridge and Professsor Peter Haggett, the equally eminent human geographer, from the University of Bristol. Professor Chorley chaired the morning session of the seminar, and, drawing on his experiences as a youngster in Minehead, memorably regaled the audience at dinner. It was Professor Haggett who first suggested the seminar, brought we two principal organisers together and also provided the summing up at the seminar. Together the two have written the excellent introduction to this book and kindly served as the overseeing editorial committee. As organisers, we were especially pleased to have them participating so fully, as we were both taught by them during our student years at Cambridge! Our thanks also go to Rachel Thomas, a Countryside Commissioner, who has been intimately associated with the Park over the last two decades and who ably chaired the afternoon session of the seminar, kindly served on the organising committee and has provided a thought provoking and forward looking concluding chapter to this book.

We are also very grateful to our sponsors, the South Western Electricity Board and the Nationwide Building Society. The former provided a fee for each of the speakers and chairpersons, and funds for both the folders given to each participant and for editing this book, while the latter has paid for the provision of colour illustrations. Their generous support has helped defray the cost of the seminar itself and of this subsequent publication and we have been extremely pleased to have them associated with us in this venture. Our task in organising the event was also made easier by the work of our colleagues on the committee: Rachel Thomas, John Willett of the Royal Geographical Society and, from the Exmoor National Park Authority, Martin Evans and Alan Bailey who organised the two field days so ably, and Vicki Strutt, who did the ticketing and finance.

The background support from many others in our two organisations also made our task easier and we are especially grateful to Lord Jellicoe, President of the Royal Geographical Society, and Humphrey Temperley, Chairman of the Exmoor National Park Committee, for opening the seminar that was held in the delightful surroundings of the Carnarvon Arms Hotel near Dulverton. Finally our thanks go to Hilary Binding for her excellent work in editing this publication.

For the Royal Geographical Society this was our most ambitious regional event to date. The Society was founded in 1830 with the objective, still current today, of 'the improvement and diffusion of geographical knowledge', and this has kept it at the forefront of all matters of geographical and exploration activity. In 1989 the Society established five regions, which organise lectures, seminars and field-days outside London to supplement the London-based programme. The most successful of the regions has been the Western one centred on Bristol, which led in 1994 to the setting up of a sixth region for the South West covering West Somerset, Devon and Cornwall because the former single region was so large. The South West Region has been particularly pleased to collaborate with the National Park not only in organising the seminar, but in producing this publication for enjoyment by a much wider audience and as a spur to further research on Exmoor. It is also appropriate that this should happen in the same year that the Royal Geographical Society has merged with the Institute of British Geographers.

With regard to the Exmoor National Park, the symposium has not only provided an additional event to help celebrate the fortieth anniversary, but also has assisted in establishing a stronger link with geographers and researchers in the region in a wide range of disciplines which we hope will lead to greater and more fruitful collaboration in the future. It has also contributed to the National Park Authority's increasing interest in environmental education, providing students and others with sound information about the area.

The link between the Royal Geographical Society and Exmoor National Park Authority was fostered initially by the late Leonard Curtis, who was National Park Officer from 1978-88 and himself an academic geographer of considerable reputation. His insight and pioneering work was an inspiration to several of the speakers and it is fitting that this book should be dedicated to him. We sincerely hope this publication will help inspire more interest in research on Exmoor, as he would have wished, and with his example as a guiding light.

David Rabson, Deputy National Park Officer, ENPA
John Russell, Chairman, SW Region, RGS
Co-organisers of the Symposium

Duty Point from Castle Rock. (Courtesy Linda Sheard.)

EXMOOR: AN INTRODUCTION

Richard Chorley (*Professor of Geography, University of Cambridge*)
and Peter Haggett (*Professor of Urban and Regional Geography, University of Bristol*)

Once in his life a man ought to concentrate his mind upon the remembered earth. He ought to give himself up to a particular landscape of his experience, to look at it from as many angles as he can, to wonder about it, to dwell upon it. He ought to imagine that he touches it with his hands at every season...to recollect all the colours of the dawn and dusk.

N.Scott Momaday
The Way to Rainy Mountain [1969].

For both of us Exmoor is a 'remembered' landscape. Both our childhoods and our schooldays were spent in West Somerset: one of us was born, grew up and went to school on the northern fringes of the moor in the Somerset coastal town of Minehead. For the other, the bulk of Exmoor was a hazy outline glimpsed around the shoulder of the Quantocks only on a day of exceptional clarity. Whatever that early exposure meant, the hill country of West Somerset must have left an abiding memory on both of us for when we went on to Oxbridge we both chose to write our undergraduate dissertations on Exmoor and Quantock themes.

So for both of us it was a particular pleasure to be asked to take part in the celebrations of the fortieth anniversary of the Exmoor National Park. The day-long sessions at Dulverton in September 1994 looked at Exmoor from many different angles and it's these contributions which form the basis for this welcome book. Our job in this brief introduction is simply to share some thoughts that arose from listening to the papers and now rereading them in their present form. Seven points strike us as important and we take each in turn.

First, we have much still to learn about Exmoor. Although England is one of the most thoroughly studied of English landscapes much of our knowledge of Exmoor is surprisingly recent. Even in geology, the most grandfatherly of the environmental sciences, the earliest papers considering Exmoor are less than two centuries old with Horner (1816) and De la Beche (1839) amongst the earliest.

Second, much of what we 'know' about Exmoor may eventually be proved to be wrong. It was the American humorist, Will Rogers, who used to complain that what worried him was not the things he didn't know but '...those things I know, which ain't so'. We see in Exmoor the old certainties of one generation of scholars being replaced by new certainties of another. Balchin's (1952) careful assessment of a flight of erosion surfaces ranging from the 'summit' surface of the sub-Cretaceous down to the 'Instow' surface of late-Pliocene age now seems highly unlikely in the light of the increasing data on Exmoor's unstable tectonic history (Hancock, 1983). The river capture model of one paper (Penning-Rowsell, 1974) may have to be reassessed in the light of new knowledge on ice-sheet margins and glacial ponding of another (Hawkins, 1977). Allan Straw's opening essay gives a scholarly review of such changes and reinterpretations while Heather Wilson shows how many puzzles remain to be solved in Exmoor's complex but beautiful coastal geomorphology.

Third, each phase of human occupation has found in Exmoor new resources and new challenges. Edward Maltby's chapter

9

shows how Bronze Age communities failed to cope with Exmoor conditions and left behind their own environmental planning disasters. Veryan Heal and Vanessa Straker show how the manmade Exmoor landscapes from the mesolithic communities of Porlock Bay to the medieval farmsteads of the Exe Valley were shaped by successive communities coping with Exmoor's possibilities and problems. Hilary Binding takes that theme on into recent economic history of Exmoor. The iron ore extraction in the Brendon Hills which led to the mineral line engineering works of the mid-nineteenth century and the stone quarrying of the late twentieth century are but two examples of more recent resource exploitation of Exmoor.

Fourth, the need to be continually monitoring change on Exmoor. One of the legacies of Len Curtis' work (1971) was to set up benchmarks against which soil changes can be set. Andrew Harrison's lecture showed how remote sensing imagery and geographical information systems allow the present structure of Exmoor land use to be mapped and monitored in ways undreamed of by our predecessors.

Fifth, the historical record underlines the need to keep our options open in planning Exmoor's future. The historical sweep of the essays contained in this volume show that Exmoor has changed greatly in the past and will change greatly in the future. To reduce it to some kind of heritage park would have short-term benefits but long-term problems. Both Mark Blacksell's essay on Exmoor planning and Stephen Essex's study of Exmoor woodland show how external political debates in Whitehall have impinged on local decisions. With increasing European integration the forces which affect Exmoor land use are likely to come from ever further afield.

Sixth, we note the practical importance of resource partnerships for the study of Exmoor. The linking of the Royal Geographical Society with the Exmoor National Park Authority in organizing this meeting; the interest of universities from nearby Bristol, Plymouth and Exeter to London; the resources provided by the South Western Electricity Board and the Nationwide Building Society.

Seventh, we need visions and overarching concepts if we are to

plan for Exmoor. From a scientific standpoint, we think one of the most useful ones, and one which pervades many papers in this volume, is to regard Exmoor as being in a dynamic steady-state. On this view, the Exmoor landscape as we see it today is held in place only by a fragile balance between powerful forces, themselves subject to change. Some of those forces will change gradually and slowly and over long periods of time; others will change much more quickly than we can now conceive.

We hope that one of the outcomes of this book will be to attract new researchers to Exmoor for there are many of its mysteries still waiting to be solved. There are few better starting points for a newcomer than Selworthy Beacon: from there we can see many of the landscapes which are described in this book. Eastwards the view along the whaleback ridge of North Hill extends towards the town of Minehead, hidden in its lee with, beyond, the fertile Dunster marshes and the seaward slopes of the Brendon and Quantock ranges. Southwards lies the steep descent into the Selworthy valley and the rise towards Dunkery and the Exmoor uplands. Westwards, the crescent shingle of Porlock Bay and the hump-backed cliffs stretch away towards Lynmouth. Northwards, the steep slopes of Bossington Hill plunge towards the steel-grey waters of the Bristol Channel with the distant Welsh coastline beyond.

If the day is an inclement one (and Exmoor has its share) then stop at the small 'wind and weather hut' below the crest of Selworthy Beacon. It was built of local sandstone and erected as a memorial to Sir Thomas Dyke Acland (1787-1871) by his family. The spot was chosen by Acland's youngest surviving son, by then living in Holnicote, New Zealand, to mark the precise destination of family walks. Each Sunday afternoon, Acland, with his children and later his grandchildren, would walk up the combe from the Acland family home at Holnicote in the valley below. On the western end of the hut is carved a few lines from John Keble (1792-1866), the Oxford poet and theologian, which include the phrase '...where the landscape in its glory, teaches truth to wandering men'. Exmoor has drawn to this Dulverton meeting many wandering men and women, most of whom have work that lies far from Exmoor but are drawn back to it by this fortieth anniversary. We know any truths we have been taught here will be provisional ones.

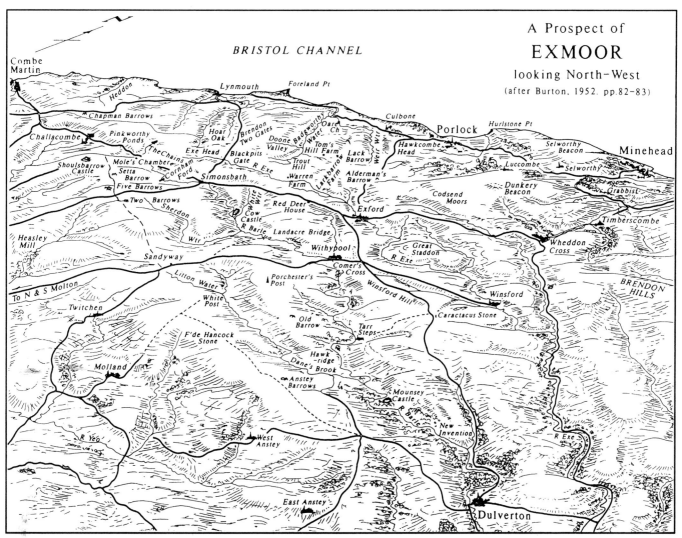

Figure 1 *A prospect of Exmoor.*

REFERENCES

W.G.V. Balchin, 'The erosion surfaces of Exmoor and adjacent areas'. *Geographical Journal*, 68, (1952) 453-476.

L.F. Curtis, *Soils of Exmoor Forest*, Harpenden: Soil Survey of England and Wales.(1971).

H.T. De la Beche, *Report on the Geology of Cornwall, Devon and West Somerset*. (1839).

P.L. Hancock,(ed.), *The Variscan Fold Belt in the British Isles*. (Bristol, 1983).

A.B. Hawkins, 'The quaternary of the North Somerset area' in R.J.G.Savage (ed.) *Geological Excursions in the Bristol District*. (Bristol, 1977).

L. Horner, 'Sketch of the geology of the southwestern part of Somersetshire'. *Transactions of the Geological Society of London*, 3 (1816), 338-384.

E.C. Penning-Rowsell, 'Historical changes in river patterns near Holford, Somerset'. *Proceedings of the Somerset Archaeological and Natural History Society*, 118 (1974), 39-43.

ACKNOWLEDGEMENT

Efforts to trace the copyright owners of the Burton map on page 11 have proved unsuccessful. The publisher would be pleased to hear from them.

ASPECTS OF THE GEOMORPHOLOGY OF EXMOOR

Allan Straw

Reardon Smith Professor of Geography, University of Exeter

INTRODUCTION

The Exmoor landscape is one of innumerable contrasts deriving from its unique mix of farmland, woodland, moorland and physiography. The product of millenia of human activity, the cultural landscape variously softens or sharpens, conceals or reveals the valleys, hills and rivers which comprise the physical landscape away from the coast. These landforms and rivers have a much longer history than the human features and the ensuing discussion will examine some of them and

ERA		PERIOD	MILLIONS YEARS BP
QUATERNARY		Holocene	0.01
		Pleistocene	2
TERTIARY	Neogene	Pliocene	6
		Miocene	24
	Palaeogene	Oligocene	32
		Eocene	51
		Palaeocene	65
MESOZOIC		Cretaceous	135
		Jurassic	205
		Triassic	250
		Permian	290
PALAEOZOIC		Carboniferous	360
		Devonian	400

Figure 2 Geological sequence and timescale.

suggest reasons for their existence. Reference should be made to Figure 2 for the geological sequence and timescale.

It is over forty years since Balchin's paper on Exmoor erosion surfaces was published in the Geographical Journal (1952) and, surprisingly perhaps, no other comprehensive account of the geomorphology of Exmoor has succeeded it. It has been included in various overviews of South West England (Wooldridge, 1954; Balchin, 1964; Gregory, 1969; Simpson, 1969; Coque-Delhuille, 1991) but little new material on Exmoor was offered. Balchin's paper remains therefore a yardstick for reappraisal of the geomorphology of Exmoor and it prompts four observations.

1. It was claimed that Exmoor had experienced marine submergence to a height of 1225 feet OD (373 m) early in the Neogene (Miocene) followed by a phased recession.

2. A very large number of interfluve fragments or `flats' of erosion surfaces were identified and interpreted as vestiges of wavecut platforms many millions of years old.

3. It was assumed that Exmoor had `stood proud' relative to central Devon and the Bristol Channel area throughout the Tertiary era.

4. No attempt was made to relate the shaping of Exmoor to the development of the Bristol Channel and insufficient notice seems to have been taken of Jones' 1930 paper.

GEOLOGICAL BACKGROUND

Geological studies of both the Bristol Channel and Exmoor have burgeoned since 1952 (Webby, 1965 a, b; Shearman, 1967; Owen, 1971; Lloyd et al, 1973; Fletcher, 1975; Palmer, 1975; Evans and Thompson, 1979; Selwood and Durrance, 1982; Edmonds et al, 1985; Edmonds and Williams, 1985), and it is now certain that aspects of structural geology have great relevance to the very existence as well as the form of Exmoor. The more significant facts are as follows.

1. Exmoor, composed of marine and continental Devonian rocks (Figure 3), is an integral part of the Cornubian platform blocked out by major Hercynian earth movements in late Carboniferous/early Permian time.

2. Subsequent to folding and faulting Exmoor, as part of this platform, was initially a zone of high mountains which suffered immense erosion through Permian and Triassic times, with thick deposits mainly of Mercia Mudstone (Keuper Marl) accumulating in the fault-bounded troughs of Porlock and Minehead, in the Bristol Channel and eastward into Somerset. The end-Trias land surface was eventually submerged by Jurassic seas, but uplift followed by erosion through most of the Cretaceous period probably stripped away all earlier Mesozoic rocks from Exmoor. Late submergence permitted deposition of a thin cover of Chalk which Tertiary erosion has since removed.

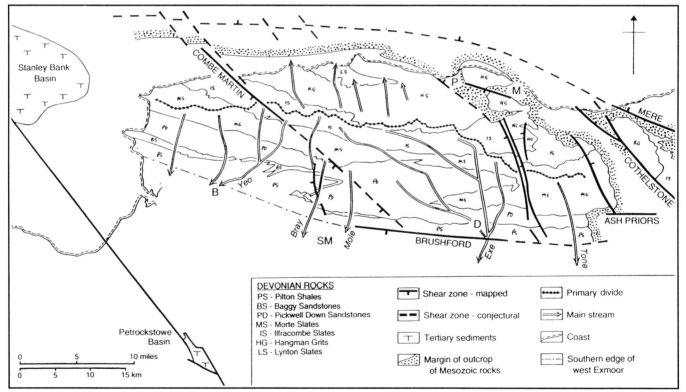

Figure 3 Geology and drainage of Exmoor (B – Barnstaple; D – Dulverton; M – Minehead; P – Porlock; SM – South Molton).

3. The Bristol Channel has had a complex geological history. Following the Hercynian orogeny it was a land area, albeit lowlying, between, and continuous with, Cornubia to the south and Wales to the north. Subsidence in mid-Triassic time possibly as a graben (Audley-Charles, 1992) allowed accumulation of Mercia Mudstone produced by erosion of Cornubia and Wales to thicknesses of 300 m. Marine flooding from the west in the Jurassic, related to early stages of Atlantic opening, permitted deposition of some 2170 m of rocks from Lias through to Kimmeridge Clay (Evans and Thompson, 1979).

At times during the early part of the Cretaceous period the Bristol Channel region was again part of a land area of low relief which was flooded late in the period to receive Chalk sediments. Emergence at the beginning of the Tertiary era restored terrestrial conditions until mid-Tertiary (Miocene) earth movements caused the Channel to sink and be flooded once again along its synclinal axes and within bounding faults or flexures.

Exmoor is underlain almost exclusively by Middle and Upper Devonian rocks disposed mainly on the southern limb of an east-pitching anticline (Figure 3) the axis of which runs east-south-east through Lynton (Selwood and Durrance, 1982; Edmonds et al, 1985). The northern limb extends beneath the Bristol Channel and Devonian rocks underlie the Channel floor for a mile or two before giving way to Mesozoic rocks (Figure 3) which soon drop steeply across a major strike fault (Lloyd et al, 1973) or pronounced flexure (Evans and Thompson, 1979) into the major syncline which preserves thicknesses of over 2400 m. West of Exmoor, beyond the coast, Devonian rocks descend gently beneath the deep Tertiary Stanley Bank basin (Figure 3) developed like those to the southeast at Petrock-stowe and Bovey along the Sticklepath wrench fault system (Dearman, 1963; Fletcher, 1975; Edwards and Freshney, 1982).

In east Exmoor the anticlinal structure is dislocated by several large faults including those which determine the Trias-floored vales south-east of Porlock and Minehead, and the mini-horsts of Bossington Hill and the Quantocks (Webby, 1965a, b) (Figure 3). More importantly the Devonian outcrop is terminated east of the Quantocks by a prominent fault zone which extends from the Mere fault in Somerset (Palmer, 1975) and most probably passes into the major structure north of Exmoor (Owen, 1971).

On the south side the junction between the folded Devonian and Carboniferous rocks is accompanied by much strike-slip faulting. One such fault, the Brushford fault, marks precisely the southern border of Exmoor as a relief unit (Figures 3, 4) from South Molton to Brushford and perhaps Milverton. West-north-west from South Molton to Braunton, the Exmoor border has an equally remarkable linear character suggesting structural control though no fault has been mapped.

THE UPLAND PLATEAUX

Exmoor is undoubtedly plateau country although dissected substantially by its main rivers and their tributaries. On the south side, Molland Common and the Haddon Hills on Pickwell Down Sandstones reach 350 m or more above sea-level. In the east the Brendon Hills on Morte Slates reach over 400 m OD and Dunkery Hill on Hangman Grits to the northwest touches 519 m OD. Westward in Exmoor Forest, ground over 400 m OD occurs on a variety of rock groups (Plate 1). Over an area therefore of some 800 km² the higher parts of Exmoor, showing a gentle declination from north-west to south-east, reach heights that range only within some 150 m (Figure 4).

Overall it is this remarkable accordance which is *the* impressive Exmoor feature – not a multiplicity of 'flats' and 'surfaces' but this one upland plain that transects all rock types. North of the primary divide (Figure 4) it survives on Lucott Moor (465 m) (Plate 2) and Brendon Common (423 m), and eastward of the faults perhaps on the higher parts of Bossington Hill (300 m) and of the Quantocks (310-380 m).

What however of west Exmoor? West of a line between Combe Martin and Molland the summit areas rarely exceed 300 m and have an average height of only 275 m OD (Figure 4) yet the Devonian rocks here are no different in general from those to the east. The plateau character persists but altitudinally the

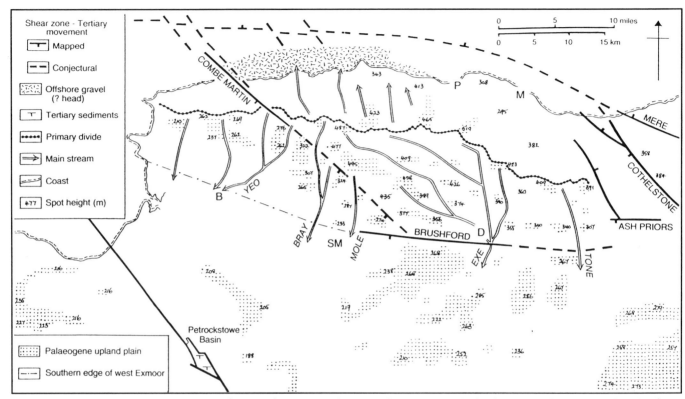

Figure 4 *The upland plain and drainage of Exmoor (B – Barnstaple; D – Dulverton; M – Minehead; P – Porlock; SM – South Molton).*

affinity of west Exmoor is with central Devon. Excepting the lower ground around the lower Taw and Torridge rivers and their tributaries which has developed since the subsidence of the Stanley Bank basin (Straw, 1986), an equally striking interfluve surface occurs across highly-folded Carboniferous rocks between 210 and 290 m OD. Not only do west Exmoor and central Devon display a common plateau level but certain rivers like the Mole and Bray are shared as well.

Why, then, does high Exmoor stand above west Exmoor? If Devonian rocks were planed at about 275 m OD in the west why not in the centre and east as well? Why does high Exmoor stand above central Devon? The planation of west Exmoor indicates that the Devonian rocks are no more resistant

generally than the Carboniferous ones, so why does Exmoor form an upland at all? What are the ages of the plateau surfaces in high Exmoor on the one hand and in west Exmoor/central Devon on the other? What clues to or confirmation of land-forming events can be obtained from the drainage pattern?

AGE AND DISLOCATION OF THE UPLAND PLATEAUX

The age of the west Exmoor/central Devon plateau surface can be considered first. The Petrockstowe basin is one of several developed along the Sticklepath fault (Figure 3). Its contained sediments accumulated to a depth of some 760 m (Edwards and Freshrey, 1982) and are entirely alluvial showing that deposition kept pace with the rate of subsidence of the basin.

16

Plate 1 View ESE from SS 751374. Dipslope of Morte Slates gives way to the Hangley Cleave escarpment of Pickwell Down Sandstones. Skyline is formed by the upland plain at 435-455 m OD.

Plate 2 View WNW from SS 891416. Primary divide W from Dunkery Beacon at 500 m OD, with Lucott Moor (460 m) forming the skyline on the N side. Convex slopes reveal the effect of gelifluction.

The sediments are largely derived from Carboniferous rocks deeply weathered under a sub-tropical climate and are mostly of fine grade having been transported and emplaced by very low gradient rivers. They accumulated through the middle and late Eocene and the Oligocene over a period of about twenty million years (Figure 2), accompanied by extensive planation of surrounding land areas. The central Devon plateau is the only relevant large-scale feature to represent that planation (Straw, 1986). It would have been a plain of very low relief by the end of the Oligocene drained generally to the southeast by a river system substantially similar to that suggested by Jones (1930) and reconstructed by Wooldridge (1954). The streams flowing south off west Exmoor confirm that the plateau formerly extended onto the Devonian rocks rising gently to the primary divide between Woolacombe and Kentisbury. Jones (1930) regarded the plateau as an end-Trias surface and Coque-Delhuille (1991) considered it part of a 'Devon-Cornwall' surface ascribing it to a Lower Cretaceous transgression. However, the simplest geomorphological interpretation is that the plateau is not an exhumed landform but rather a Palaeogene feature produced by sub-aerial erosion which was never subsequently submerged nor covered by more recent sediments.

If this age is accepted, does the high Exmoor plateau represent an even earlier Palaeogene planation? Is it an exhumed Mesozoic surface planed during Cretaceous or Jurassic transgressions or by Triassic pediplanation or is it a pre-Permian, post-Hercynian feature (Balchin, 1964; Simpson, 1969; Coque-Delhouille, 1991)? A reconsideration of the geological evidence shows that it is most probably none of these.

In east Exmoor large faults (Webby 1965a, 1965b; Edmonds and Williams 1985) border the graben-like vales. Much lateral and vertical movement took place before and during the Trias, but some displacement is manifestly post-Jurassic e.g. the Watchet fault (Whittaker 1972), and it is generally conceded that Tertiary movement could have occurred on any of them. Most important is the Mere fault east of the Quantocks, throwing down northeast, which curves westward, parallel to the Exmoor coast, where it has a downthrow north of some 450 m (Lloyd et al, 1973).

On the west, Shearman (1967) has shown that the Combe Martin shear zone is not only one of the family of dextral wrench faults of Devon (Dearman 1963) but extends southeast across Exmoor (Figures 3, 4) and is in all probability responsible not only for offsetting rock outcrops but for initiating the steep west-facing bluff that marks the descent from the high plateau. He suggests a downthrow of 155 m to the south-west.

The southern margin of Exmoor is everywhere sharply delineated physiographically. East of South Molton it is determined by the Brushford fault, significantly east of where the Combe Martin fault leaves Exmoor. Although essentially a strike-slip feature, vertical movement of some 70 m is indicated.

In summary, high Exmoor constitutes a rhomboid block of mainly Devonian rocks defined by shear zones for all of which some mid-Tertiary (post-Oligocene) displacement can be demonstrated or argued. While reference has deliberately been to downthrow on the faults, it is the upthrow that is relevant and the inescapable conclusion is that high Exmoor is high because it has been raised by some 150-200 m as a horst. If so, before such elevation, its plateau surface was most probably an integral part of the central Devon/west Exmoor Oligocene plain.

RIVERS AND VALLEYS

Reference has been made by many authors to the Exmoor rivers (Clayden, 1906; Balchin, 1952; Wooldridge, 1954; Shearman, 1967; Simpson, 1969; Edmonds et al, 1985), and not least to the alleged superimposed nature of the drainage systems. In most cases superimposition has been assumed from a Chalk cover but, if the plateau is end-Oligocene and had been produced largely under subtropical, and at times semi-arid conditions, the drainage at that time may have borne little resemblance to any original streams on the Chalk. Wooldridge (1954) drew attention to the position of the primary divide of South West England (Figures 3, 4), arguing that it was close to the northern margin of the Cornubian block and determined by its end-Cretaceous uplift. Jones (1930) had previously argued that it was created by mid-Tertiary arching of Exmoor.

However, the Bristol Channel was a land area through Palaeogene time (Cope et al, 1992, Maps Pg1-Pg3) and would surely have had a complementary drainage system to that of Devon (Figure 5a). The primary divide may therefore be geomorphologically rather than tectonically determined, especially since it passes from Morte Slates in the east over Ilfracombe Slates to Hangman Grits at Dunkery Hill and thence westward back to Morte Slates near Woolacombe (Plate 2).

From this divide a number of streams, reflecting generally the slope of the Oligocene plain, drain south across Exmoor onto Carboniferous or Trias rocks (Yeo, Bray/Mole, Exe, Tone) and north to the coast (Badgworthy Water, Farley Water, West Lyn, Heddon) (Figure 4). The northerly streams are now obviously shorter and more steeply graded, but the old divide has been displaced only where a Quarme headwater has been captured by the River Avill at Wheddon Cross and by fluvial exploitation of the faults and Trias vales in and north of the Brendon Hills. Such few adjustments confirm that the vigour of these northern streams is a relatively recent phenomenon. In part low Pleistocene sea-levels may have encouraged valley-deepening but shortening of stream courses has probably been more effective in causing incision in the longer term. The end-Oligocene plain of the Bristol Channel area, descending north from the primary divide (Figure 5a), would have been developed on Triassic and Jurassic as well as Devonian rocks. In the Miocene the Bristol Channel and central Devon became depressed by faulting relative to high Exmoor, the Channel the more so, so that by late Miocene time it could be flooded by the encroaching Atlantic (Figure 5b). The original north-flowing rivers were therefore shortened by faulting and flooding and given a lower base-level than those draining south. Marine erosion has also pared back the northern margin of Exmoor some three to five miles from the fault to the present coastline. Several of the north-draining valleys between Ilfracombe and Minehead may therefore be the rejuvenated heads of drainage developed on the original Oligocene surface.

In such a pattern the Lyn valley system is obviously an anomaly because substantial elements of it are aligned broadly parallel to the coast and to the Devonian strike. Much attention has been drawn in the past to that section known as the Valley

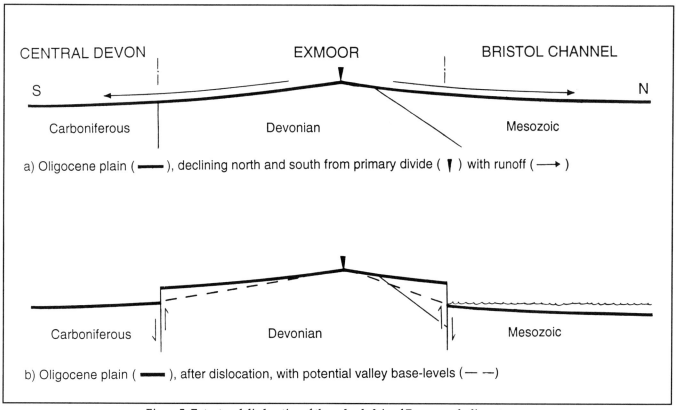

S   N

Carboniferous   Devonian   Mesozoic

a) Oligocene plain (▬), declining north and south from primary divide (▼) with runoff (→)

Carboniferous   Devonian   Mesozoic

b) Oligocene plain (▬), after dislocation, with potential valley base-levels (─ ─)

Figure 5 Extent and dislocation of the upland plain of Exmoor and adjacent areas.

of Rocks (Clayden, 1906; Simpson, 1953; Mottershead, 1964; Dalzell and Durrance, 1980). Broken by cliff recession and grossly modified by periglacial processes it is nevertheless of fluvial origin. All authors have been impressed by the alignment of the East Lyn valley with the Valley of Rocks and have sought by diverse arguments to demonstrate that the Lyn formerly reached the sea by way of either Wringcliff or Lee Bays. However these gaps, currently outlets for runoff (and formerly for evacuation of gelifluctate materials or 'head') serve only modified sections of the valley. Of much more import is that part of the Valley (Plate 3) between the cemetery (SS 714494) and Lynton School (SS 721494) because it is largely unmodified, is the oldest and descends gently east through Lynton. The original stream seems therefore to have flowed eastward, not westward, from headwaters on Martinhoe Common and perhaps over Woody Bay to Lynton. There it joined the West and East Lyn rivers and flowed northward. However, demonstration that the West Lyn represents an original north-flowing drainage element does not explain why major tributaries from east and west exist.

For one or two miles offshore, Devonian rocks form the sea floor but are then covered by Mesozoic rocks (Figure 3) which, at the major west-east dislocation, thicken rapidly into the Bristol Channel syncline (Lloyd et al, 1973). Whether or not such rocks ever covered Exmoor prior to, and even after,

Plate 3 View ES from SS 710495. Lynton section of the
Valley of Rocks, which declines towards the Lyn Valley.
Area is underlain by Lynton Slates.

Plate 4 View ESE from SS 859404. Strike-aligned valley of
the upper River Quarme. Dipslope of Hangman Grits gives
way to escarpment of Ilfracombe Slates which rises to 400 m OD.
The river is reworking gelifluction deposits.

Miocene faulting they must have extended further toward the primary divide beneath the end-Oligocene surface (Figure 5a). Following uplift of high Exmoor they could have been pared back to form a south-facing escarpment sufficiently high and persistent to deflect north-flowing streams draining the higher Devonian ground. It is postulated therefore that the Valley of Rocks and East Lyn/Oare Water streams developed along the foot of a Mesozoic scarp to carry the drainage to a single gap over the site of Lynmouth. Their courses became so incised into the underlying Devonian rocks that there they remain, long after the Mesozoic scarp has disappeared.

Post-Oligocene elevation of high Exmoor and development of the Taw-Torridge lowlands have clearly provided opportunities for streams to incise and dissect the Palaeogene upland plain. Over some twenty million years (Figure 2) a dense network of valleys has evolved, highly adjusted to geology, bringing most of the land surface under slope. Geological control on meso-landforms is evident in the high frequency of escarpments and of slopes reflecting closely the dips of bedding or cleavage (Plates 1,4). Webby (1965a), Shearman

(1967) and Edmonds et al (1985) have described many examples and geological mapping has also revealed a substantial proportion of valley orientations to be fault-controlled e.g. the Bradiford Water and River Bray in west Exmoor and the West Lyn and its neighbours on high Exmoor. Three particular sets of faults can be noted. East/west faults are essentially strike-slip features within the Devonian strata. North-west/south-east faults are associated with the major dextral wrench faults of Devon and occur in profusion over the Exmoor area (Edmonds et al, 1985). North-east/south-west faults are ancillary to the main wrench faults and appear to have more influence on valley direction in east Exmoor and the Brendon Hills.

PERIGLACIAL DEPOSITS AND LANDFORMS

Because Exmoor escaped glaciation during the Pleistocene period, fluvial and complementary mass-wasting processes have been paramount in dissecting the massif and, excluding losses by marine erosion, in removing rock-waste. For most of

Plate 5 *View NE from SS 783480 of Ashton Cleave in the East Lyn Valley 2km E of Brendon. Screen-veneered slopes on the N side, bare where reactivated.*

Plate 6 *View SSE from SS 746452 of the Farley Water valley. The valley bifurcates around Alse Burrow; the stream occupies the E branch. Gelifluction materials mantle the slopes and in the valley floor are being eroded and reworked into terraces by the stream.*

the last twenty million years fluvial activity occurred under humid, warm to cool, temperate climates which permitted chemical weathering, soil formation and a woodland vegetation cover, but during the past two million years of the Pleistocene period different environmental conditions, Arctic and Sub-Arctic in character, have dominated. Warm interglacial periods have been short, of the order of twenty to thirty thousand years, and the cumulative effect of the cold periods with geomorphological processes dominated by physical weathering under a largely treeless vegetation cover has been very substantial (Waters, 1965). All of Exmoor has been subject to frost action and geliturbation and snowmelt from summer thaw has encouraged near ubiquitous gelifluction. The steeper valley sides where not actively undercut usually carry screes (Plate 5), and valley-floor deposits are dominated by coarse bed-load gravels or partly reworked gelifluction materials (Plates 4, 6).

The scale of such periglacial impact is difficult to measure but a few contrasting examples out of many can be noted. In the Valley of Rocks, Dalzell and Durrance (1980) proved a gelifluction infill of over 30 m in the regraded section of the Valley through the car-park, but a vastly greater amount of rock-waste must have disappeared seaward to produce that regrading. At the back of Lee Bay some 18 m of 'head' overlies stream gravels. At West Porlock a shelving terrace of 'head' over 500 m wide lies along the foot of the steep Devonian slopes, but at Porlock Weir much has been lost to wave erosion. Eastward it gives way to two large coalescing fans of coarse gravel discharged by the Porlock stream and Horner Water. Lloyd et al (1973) refer to large spreads of gravel masking bedrock in the offshore zone between Ilfracombe and Foreland Point, most likely of periglacial origin (Figure 4). These thick deposits are impressive but deceptive in that they only represent bodies of material that were in transport or being aggraded when the last (Devensian) cold stage ceased some ten thousand years ago. So too are the 'heads', often no more than 1 m thick (Plate 7), that mantle moderate valley and interfluve slopes, because their very thinness is most probably a consequence of rapid downslope transport, not relative inactivity on those slopes. Rates of gelifluction in high latitudes today can be as high as 30 cm each year and cold conditions

Plate 7 View N at SS 881343 on Contisbury Common. 1.5 m of geifluctate (head) formed from and resting on Hangman Grit.

prevailed for much of the preceding hundred thousand years of the Devensian stage. Over a dozen such cold stages occurred earlier in the Pleistocene period so it would not be unreasonable to claim that periglacial conditions have, cumulatively, affected Exmoor for over one million years.

The Punchbowl (SS 883344) is the semi-hemispherical head of a short valley on the northeast side of Winsford Hill within the outcrop of Pickwell Down Sandstones. It is deep, very steep-sided and unique in form in Exmoor. Its floor is occupied by a small bog retained behind a slight ridge of probably unconsolidated rock-waste that has been breached by the stream draining the bog (Plate 8). Its shape is quite unlike the normal spring-fed ravine of Exmoor and there is no evidence of major landsliding or subsidence. The bog is a temperate deposit of the current Flandrian stage and the Punchbowl had clearly attained its size and form by the end of the Devensian cold stage. Although it no doubt originated as a small ravine like others along the ridge to the west-north-west, it surely represents a fine example of a nivation hollow, the site of heavy snow accumulation and melting accompanied by frost action. If it had reached a size sufficient for occupation by a permanent snow patch within which some internal deformation was

Plate 8 View NNE from SS 881343 into the Punchbowl on the NE side of Winsford Hill. The steep backslope descends to the bog (bottom right) which is covered by tussock grass, sedge and Salix bushes. A slight ridge is marked by the line of trees which extends across the centre of the photograph and off right.

possible, it is, perhaps, Exmoor's sole instance of an incipient glacial corrie.

In several Exmoor valleys discontinuous ridges and knolls of bedrock protrude from the valley floors. Good examples occur in the Oare Water, Barle and Exe valleys. Some are created at stream confluences when the tip of a spur, possibly crossed by a fault, is detached by the lateral erosion of a main stream and its tributary on either side of the spur as in the Weir Water valley (SS 8229463) (Plate 9). Others are determined by removal of weaker materials from around resistant strata usually steeply-dipping and often transected by faults or joints. Excellent examples lie in the Exe valley above and below Warren Farm (SS 795408) (Plate 10) and in the upper Barle below Pinkery Farm (SS 725407) and at Cornham Ford (SS 749382). Others are more problematical, for example Alse Burrow in the Farley Water valley (SS 749447) (Plate 6) which is a broad, flattish-topped mound between two mini-valleys almost of equal depth though the easterly one contains the stream and the other is floored by 'head'. All these features would seem to have arisen through fluvial and mass-wasting

Plate 10 *View ESE from SS 801403 of a valley-floor knoll (Long Barrow) in the valley of the River Exe, 1.5km below Warren Farm. The knoll is developed in Ilfracombe Slates dipping steeply S, with the river on the N side.*

processes. Most are the consequences of differential erosion on strata of varying resistance but some, like Alse Burrow, probably involve 'cut and fill' sequences when substantial thicknesses of 'head', or of gravel built up, by a braided stream system, from excessive rock-waste provided by gelifluction, are then eroded by a single channel stream under more temperate conditions.

Slope modification, valley creation and enlargement, and transport of rock-waste have obviously occurred on a very large scale through the Pleistocene period and have contributed hugely to the adjustment of valleys in their alignment and form to bedrock lithology and structure. Not surprisingly such an assessment of the profound impact of periglaciation on Exmoor increases scepticism concerning the survival for millions of years of remnants of wave-cut erosion surfaces as identified by Balchin (1952). Jones, in the Discussion to that paper, warned then of the effect of periglacial processes and noted the close control of what he termed 'pitch-faulting' on breaks-of-slope.

Plate 9 *View SSE from SS 828465 of a valley-floor knoll in Hangmans Grits, at the junction of Weir Water valley with a small tributary from the E. Isolation of the knoll is probably the result of fluvial erosion exploiting the NNW – SSE fault which controls the alignment of the main valley.*

CONCLUSION

This paper has sought to demonstrate that central and east Exmoor constitute a fault-bounded, mid-Tertiary elevated massif which, with west Exmoor and central Devon, retains fragments of a single Oligocene land surface. Except for the fine coastline, Exmoor's landform has been sculptured sub-aerially, particularly through the cold stages of the Pleistocene. It is this land form that over the past ten thousand years has been the setting for the establishment and development of a vegetation cover, for pedogenesis and, not least, for a wide range of human activities. But that is another story.

REFERENCES

M. Audley-Charles, 'Triassic', in P. McL.D. Duff and A.J. Smith, eds., *Geology of England and Wales*, Geological Society, (1992) 307-324, .

W.G.V. Balchin, 'The erosion surfaces of Exmoor and adjacent areas', *Geographical Journal*, 118 (1952) 453-476.

W.G.V. Balchin, 'The denudation chronology of South West England' in K.F.G. Hosking and G.J. Shrimpton, eds., *Present Views of Some Aspects of the Geology of Cornwall and Devon*, Royal Geological Society of Cornwall, (1964) 267-281.

A.W. Clayden, *The History of Devonshire Scenery*, (1906) 202.

I.C.W. Cope, J.K. Ingham and P.F. Rawson, (eds.) *Atlas of Palaeogeography and Lithofacies*, Geological Society, Memoir 13. (1992).

B. Coque-Delhuille, 'The long term geomorphologic evolution of the English South-West massif (UK)', *Zeitschrift fur Geomorphologie*, 35, (1991) 65-84.

D. Dalzell and E.M. Durrance, 'The evolution of the Valley of Rocks, North Devon', *Transactions of the Institute of British Geographers*, 5, (1980) 66-79.

W.R. Dearman, 'Wrench-faulting in Cornwall and south Devon', *Proceedings of the Geologists' Association*, 74 (1963) 265-287.

E.A. Edmonds, A. Whittaker and B.J. Williams, 'Geology of the country around Ilfracombe and Barnstaple', *Memoir of the British Geological Survey*, Sheets 277 and 293, (1985) 97.

E.A. Edmonds and B.J. Williams, 'Geology of the country around Taunton and the Quantock Hills', *Memoir of the British Geological Survey*, Sheet 295, (1985) 92 .

R.A. Edwards and E.C. Freshney, 'The Tertiary sedimentary rocks' in E.M. Durrance and D.J.C. Laming, *The Geology of Devon*, University of Exeter, 9, (1982) 204-237.

D.J. Evans, and M.S. Thompson, 'The geology of the central Bristol Channel and the Lundy area, South Western Approaches, British Isles', *Proceedings of the Geologists' Association*, 90, (1979) 1-20.

B.N. Fletcher, 'A new Tertiary basin east of Lundy Island', *Journal of the Geological Society*, 131, (1975) 223-225.

K.J. Gregory, 'Geomorphology', in F. Barlow, ed., *Exeter and its Region*, University of Exeter, (1969) 27-42.

O.T. Jones, 'Some episodes in the geological history of the Bristol Channel region', *Report of the British Association for the Advancement of Science*, (1930) 57-82.

A.J. Lloyd, R.J.G. Savage, A.H. Stride and D.T. Donovan, 'The geology of the Bristol Channel floor', *Philosophical Transactions of the Royal Society*, A, 274, (1973) 595-626.

D.N. Mottershead, 'The evolution of the Valley of Rocks', *Exmoor Review* 8, (1967) 69-72.

T.R. Owen, 'The structural evolution of the Bristol Channel', *Proceedings of the Geological Society*, 1664, (1971) 289-294.

C.P. Palmer, 'Neogene structures in South-West England'. *Tertiary Times*, 2, (1975) 178-184.

E.B. Selwood, and E.M. Durrance, 'The Devonian rocks', in E.M. Durrance and D.J.C. Laming, eds.,*The Geology of Devon*, University of Exeter, (1982) 15-41.

D.J. Shearman, 'On Tertiary fault movements in north Devonshire', *Proceedings of the Geologists' Association*, 78, (1967) 555-566.

S. Simpson, 'The development of the Lyn drainage system and its relation to the origin of the coast between Combe Martin and Porlock', *Proceedings of the Geologists' Association*, 64, (1953) 14-23.

S. Simpson, 'Geology' in F. Barlow, ed., *Exeter and its Region*, University of Exeter, (1969) 5-26.

A. Straw, 'Observations on certain large scale, geomorphological features in south-west England', *Proceedings of the Ussher Society*, 6, (1986) 265-267.

R.S. Waters, 'The geomorphological significance of Pleistocene frost action in south-west England', in J.B. Whitton and P.D. Wood, eds., *Essays in Geography for Austin Miller*, University of Reading, (1965) 39-57.

B.D. Webby, 'The stratigraphy and structure of the Devonian rocks in the Brendon Hills, West Somerset', *Proceedings of the Geologists' Association*, 76, (1965a) 39-60.

B.D. Webby, 'The stratigraphy and structure of the Devonian rocks in the Quantock Hills, West Somerset', *Proceedings of the Geologists'Association*, 76, (1965b) 321-343.

A. Whittaker, 'The Watchet fault – a post-Liassic transcurrent reverse fault', *Bulletin of the Geological Survey of Great Britain*, 41, (1972) 75-80.

S.W. Wooldridge, 'The physique of the South West', *Geography*, 39, (1954) 231-242.

THE COASTAL GEOMORPHOLOGY OF EXMOOR

Heather Wilson

Deputy Warden, Leonard Wills Field Studies Centre, Nettlecombe

Exmoor's thirty-four miles of coastline makes up one third of the periphery of Exmoor National Park. Two thirds of it is in some form of public ownership, with the National Trust owning 19 miles. The Exmoor coast is particularly important because of its heaths and woodlands; maritime heaths are now rare in Western Europe. Scenically it is possibly the most impressive stretch of cliff landscape to be found anywhere in England, with much of its length characterised by 'hogs-back' cliffs which drop almost sheer from the moorland plateau to the sea. It is the inaccessibility resulting from this steepness which has largely protected the coast from visitor pressure.

The rocks of Exmoor belong to the Devonian system and were deposited between 395 million and 330 million years ago. With the exception of Porlock Bay and the stretch of coast on either side of Lynton, the rocks belong to the Hangman Grit series and consist of a mixture of sandstones, slates and conglomerates. The resistance of these rocks to marine erosion has resulted in the formation of some of the highest cliffs in England, Great Hangman, for example, standing at 244 m (800') above sea level. The sediments forming the Hangman Grit were originally deposited in a shallow sea but they have been considerably modified by subsequent earth pressures which changed the muds to slates and caused extensive folding and faulting. Evidence of these processes can be seen all along the coast, for example at the foot of the Glenthorne cliffs and at Hurlstone Point at the eastern end of Porlock Bay. Recent landslides to the west of Porlock Bay have been partially attributed to the steeply inclined bedding planes.

This recent, large scale landsliding has occurred at three locations to the west of Porlock Bay. Although the landslides have all happened where the bedding planes are inclined steeply towards the beach, historical records indicate that the cliffs had been relatively stable for over a century until 1978. One explanation for the greater instability since then is the increased frequency of exceptionally high tides.

Tides are oscillations in the surface of the sea and they are caused by the gravitational attraction of the moon and the sun on the earth's water surface. However, because of its distance from the earth of 93 million miles, the gravitational force exerted by the sun is less than that exerted by the moon which is only a quarter of a million miles away. Tidal range is least when the sun and moon are at right angles to each other with respect to the earth, that is at the first and third quarters of the moon, and greatest at full and new moon when the sun, moon and earth are in a line. The maximum range tides are referred to as springs and the minimum range tides as neaps. In some parts of the world large tidal ranges are accentuated by the shape of the coastline. The Bristol Channel is one such place, where the converging shorelines cause a reduction in surface area and therefore an increase in the amplitude of the incoming tide. As a result the Bristol Channel has the highest tidal range in Europe, exceeding 12 m at springs.

The height of tides is also affected by atmospheric pressure. The surface of the sea acts as a giant barometer with water level rising as pressure falls and vice versa. This 'inverse barometric effect' is estimated as 0.01 m for every millibar difference in pressure and in a typical British year this can add between 0.5 m and 0.7 m to mean sea level. If low atmospheric pressure coincides with spring high tides then waves can reach well above the normal tide levels. Two such tides occurred in the Bristol Channel in December 1981 and February 1990 when waves removed previously slipped debris from the foot of cliffs west of Porlock which it had formerly protected. The base of the cliffs was therefore exposed to increased wave action leading to the partial collapse of the cliff face.

The cliffs either side of Lynton are composed of the slightly older Lynton beds, a mixture of sandstones, mudstones and thin shell beds. An example of the sandstones can be seen outcropping at Castle Rocks, west of Lynton, where the bedding planes and joints have been weathered to form large rectangular blocks. The softer slates have often been eroded

back to form the series of small bays from Woody Bay to Lynmouth.

The shape of the Exmoor coast has been influenced to a large extent by processes which took place during the ice ages. During the maximum extent of the last glaciation, (about 18,000 years BP) sea level was approximately 80 m-100 m below its present level. Exmoor was south of the main ice sheet, in the periglacial zone, and freeze-thaw weathering accompanied by solifluction resulted in the accumulation of a thick deposit of periglacial head at the foot of the Exmoor cliffs. This also extended out onto the continental shelf. 'Head' is a mixture of frost-shattered stones in a clayey matrix and is still exposed at a few locations including Porlockford cliff in Porlock Bay and at Gore Point to the west of Porlock Weir.

Plate 11 *Pebble size and shape at the western end of Porlock Bay, near Gore Point.*

Plate 12 *Pebble size and shape at the eastern end of Porlock Bay, near Hurlstone Point. The difference in the size and shape of pebbles between the two ends of the bay suggests that transport has been from west to east.*

Along most of the coast the post glacial rise in sea level has eroded this periglacial deposit, releasing the frost-shattered stones for transportation along the coast. In the past this transportation has been mainly from west to east, a fact illustrated by the change in the shape and sorting of the beach material in Porlock Bay between Gore Point and Hurlstone Point and by the finding of Devonian pebbles as far east as Steart, even though the most easterly outcrop is just west of Minehead, more than 30 km away.

During the period immediately following the ending of the last ice age, the sea level rose rapidly, with wave action eroding the material deposited on the continental shelf. It also flooded areas of land as demonstrated by the submerged forest at Porlock Weir. A similar submerged forest at Blue Anchor, east of Minehead, has been dated using non-marine molluscan assemblages, as being from 7500 - 5000 BP The environment indicated by the molluscs is that of a shaded swamp with stagnant pools of water and, probably, fen woodland.

Porlock Bay is the seaward limit of a low-lying area between Exmoor to the west and North Hill (also within the National Park) to the east. A pebble beach extends across the bay from Gore Point in the west to Hurlstone Point in the east. It is approximately 5 km wide and for 3 km of its length it provides protection to the low lying area landward of the bay, an area known as Porlock Marsh. In recent years the pebble beach has been breached by the sea with increasing frequency, causing flooding of Porlock Marsh and killing stock. Serious damage has occurred twice in the last decade. The first occasion was during a severe storm in December 1981 and the second in February 1990, when a long length of the beach was demolished with 250 acres of farmland being flooded.

Recently there has been considerable debate concerning the viability of maintaining the pebble ridge as a sea defence. In 1985 Wessex Water Authority commissioned a report from Sir William Halcrow and Partners. This report considered a number of alternative solutions. The most cost-effective of these involved a proposed reconstruction of the vulnerable parts of the beach using shingle obtained from the eastern end of the bay below Hurlstone Point, an area owned by the

Plate 13 Porlock Beach looking west.

National Trust. Implementation of this scheme was prevented by objectors and a 'bay wide' study was commissioned. This was undertaken by consultants, Posford Duvivier, and was published in 1992. They proposed a number of alternative solutions ranging from 'do nothing' to 'improve standard of defence to 20 years'.

If the 'do nothing' approach were to be adopted then it is likely that a number of breaches would appear in the ridge within the next few years. The low-lying land behind would be flooded by salt water on a regular basis with uncertain ecological and landscape changes but without doubt reducing its agricultural value. However, in the long term colonisation by vegetation adapted to inundation by sea water could result in the gradual accretion of mud deposits, filtered out by the vegetation and gradually building up the level of the land. To start with, when vegetation cover was sparse this would be a slow process but as the vegetation cover became denser its efficiency in filtering and stabilising would improve until the increased height of the land would result in a decreasing frequency of inundation. In other words, in the long term, natural processes could resolve the problem.

The potential adverse impact of a 'do nothing' policy could be reduced by careful management of the area after breaches

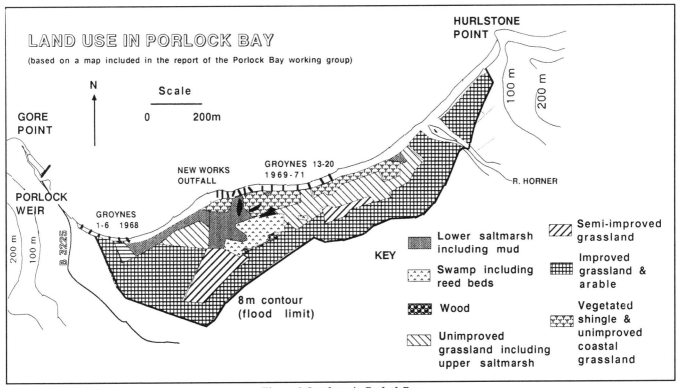

LAND USE IN PORLOCK BAY

(based on a map included in the report of the Porlock Bay working group)

N

Scale

0   200m

GORE POINT

HURLSTONE POINT

PORLOCK WEIR

B 3225

GROYNES 1-6 1968

NEW WORKS OUTFALL

GROYNES 13-20 1969-71

R. HORNER

100 m

200 m

200 m

100 m

8 m contour (flood limit)

KEY

Lower saltmarsh including mud

Swamp including reed beds

Wood

Unimproved grassland including upper saltmarsh

Semi-improved grassland

Improved grassland & arable

Vegetated shingle & unimproved coastal grassland

Figure 6 Land use in Porlock Bay.

occur. This 'managed retreat' option would be a reactive solution, depending on the characteristics of the breaches and could cost several thousands of pounds.

If the ridge itself is to be preserved, Posford Duvivier suggest that the cheapest technically viable solution would be to improve it to a 20 year standard. This means that the beach would be managed so that on average a breach is only likely to occur once in 20 years. However this would involve moving material from Bossington Beach at the eastern end of the bay and would cost around £400,000. It is questionable whether this cost would be economically justifiable.

The history of Porlock Bay indicates that the present problems largely result from natural processes but that they have been made worse by human interference. The primary problem is the loss of the supply of material feeding the beach. The original beach was almost certainly deposited a considerable distance offshore, during the period of rapidly-rising sea levels which immediately followed the ending of the last ice age. During this period erosion of the 'head' deposited on the continental shelf provided a source of beach material. When sea levels stabilised approximately 6000 years ago the rate of erosion slowed down, reducing the supply of material. In this respect the supply of material for Porlock Beach, as for many other beaches world-wide, may be virtually a process of the past.

Even without rises in sea level, gravel beaches have a natural tendency to move landwards. As the waves wash gravel over

29

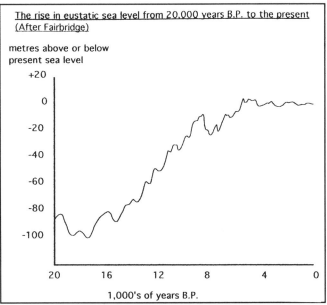

The rise in eustatic sea level from 20,000 years B.P. to the present (After Fairbridge)

metres above or below present sea level

Figure 7 The rise in eustatic sea level.

the top of the beach there are no natural processes available to return it. If the beach is between two headlands then it may become stretched as it moves landwards because the centre moves faster than the edges. Unless the stretching is accompanied by a constant supply of sediment, the beach will be thinned and may be breached by the sea at its weakest points. In addition, an inadequate supply of material may result in the sea reworking part of the beach, particularly in the updrift zones. This gradually causes a break up of the original shape into smaller units or cells, each with its own erosional and depositional zones. This is clearly happening in Porlock Bay and within the two obvious cells increased rates of erosion are leading to weakened areas, in particular east of Porlockford cliff and just east of New Works outfall.

The division of the beach into cells has probably been encouraged by the existence of the lagoons behind it. Evidence from other sites suggests that barrier retreat is slowed down by the presence of lagoons resulting in the development of 'bulges' such as that at New Works (Carter 1990). Under normal circumstances, without human interference, the beach would hold back a freshwater or slightly brackish lagoon. The

Plate 14 Collapsed pill box on Porlock Beach. As this was originally constructed behind the beach it is one of the indicators that the beach is gradually moving landwards.

Plate 15 Porlock Bay from North Hill showing the division of the bay into two cells and the 'hogs back' cliffs of Exmoor.

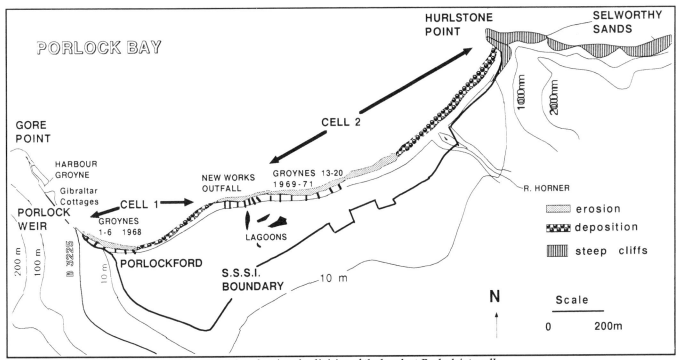

Figure 8 Map showing the division of the beach at Porlock into cells.

height of water held in the lagoon would be controlled by the sea level and the permeability of the gravel barrier with the barrier regulating the seaward drainage of freshwater. If exceptionally high tides caused the sea level to rise above the height of the lagoon, sea water would percolate landwards. Although the lagoons behind Porlock Bay have been artificially drained and the former extensive lagoon dramatically reduced in size, deposits in the remaining lagoons show evidence of repeated tidal influences in the past going back to c.6000 years BP It is therefore probable that the present breaches may simply be returning the marsh to a condition which has occurred on several previous occasions.

There is no doubt that human interference over the past 200 years has increased the problems being experienced today. For example, at Porlock Weir a near-terminal groyne has been constructed to protect the entrance to the harbour. This has intercepted the movement of material in an easterly direction causing downdrift starvation. It has also restricted the movement of material bypassing it, resulting in deposition east of the harbour mouth and in front of Gibraltar cottages. These changes have caused an alteration in the inshore wave conditions, with waves now approaching Porlockford cliff more obliquely. This change in wave direction has increased the mobility of the beach material causing thinning of the barrier. Attempts to stabilise the vulnerable parts of the ridge using groynes have been made from as early as 1824 and between 1967 and 1971 a new groyne system was installed. Most of these groynes now show a considerable depth of shingle accumulation on their western side, but in spite of some improvements they have not proved to be completely successful, often resulting in increased erosion on their eastern side.

Plate 16 *The near-terminal groyne protecting the entrance to Porlock Weir harbour.*

The ridge will continue to respond to rising sea levels, storm frequency and sediment supply. Decisions on management will always be complex due to the wide variety and number of interested bodies. The National Trust owns a large area at the eastern end of the bay while Porlock Manor Estate owns the land to the west, including the harbour and car park. The whole of the bay is within the Exmoor National Park. In addition to its agricultural quality, the land behind Porlock Bay is also valued for its conservation worth, a fact that was recognised when much of the ridge and the land behind was designated a Site of Special Scientific Interest by the Nature Conservancy Council (English Nature) in 1990.

Any management plan must now comply with the Ministry of Agriculture, Fisheries and Food's strategy document on coastal defence in England and Wales which requires that coastal processes should not be disrupted unless important assets are at risk. The evidence is that if the beach is not repaired, breaching will take place and the marsh will return to a state of salinity.

REFERENCES

R.W.G. Carter, *Coastal Environments*, (1988).

Plate 17 *Anchor groyne on Porlock Beach, showing erosion on the eastern side.*

R.W.G. Carter, *Porlock Bay – Report to the National Trust*, Unpublished (1990).

A. Clowes & P. Comfort, *Process and Landform*, (1982).

The Halcrow Report, *Suggested Sea Defences for Porlock Bay*, (1985).

Posford Duvivier, *Porlock Bay Coastal Management Study*, (1992).

Integral Geotechnique Limited, *Study of Landslipped Coastal Slopes and Woodland: Culbone Woods, Somerset*, (Bristol, 1992).

Soil Development and Ecological Change on Exmoor

Edward Maltby

Professor of Environmental and Physical Geography,
University of London

The varied nature of Exmoor's geology, landforms and climate is responsible for fundamental spatial differences in soil forming conditions. This variation has contributed significantly to the diversity of vegetation and human activities which gives rise to the National Park's unique complexity of landscapes. Within its boundaries are included some of the nation's most productive agricultural soils such as those developed on the Permo-Triassic parent materials of the Vale of Porlock. Yet, less than 20 km to the west, the plateau surface of The Chains supports one of the country's most intact blanket bogs at an altitude of 460 – 487 m with a maximum peat depth of at least 2.8 m (Merryfield & Moore, 1974).

The main area of deep peat extends east along this central plateau to Exe Plain but isolated deposits of thinner blanket peat occur on other upland surfaces generally above 400 m. Downslope from the peat-dominated summits there is frequently a more or less consistent sequence of soil types which reflects differences in drainage and microclimate. Peat thickness declines downslope and with decreasing elevation often merging imperceptibly into the peaty surface horizon of stagnohumic gleys and thin iron pan stagnopodzols occupying the shoulders of the upper valley slopes (Curtis, 1971).

Brown earth soils occupy the better drained steeper valley slopes but these, in turn, give way to gleyed brown earths in poorly drained or frequently flooded valley bottoms where peats may also accumulate in depressions and at spring sites due to the high water table. This distribution of soils is the result not only of a complex interplay of physical and environmental factors but is the outcome of significant human actions which have been of fundamental importance in determining the detailed pattern.

Nowhere else in upland Britain are there better examples of the ways in which human activities are capable of directing and re-directing the course of soil development. This paper examines the evidence for these various transformations of soils with particular reference to the upland zones of Exmoor.

Post-Glacial Soil Development

The upland surfaces some 10,000 years BP are likely to have resembled present day periglacial conditions.

Angular rock fragments resulting from frost shattering were deposited in various thicknesses, depending on the effect of solifluction, together with various types of patterned ground which characterise modern periglacial environments. These formed the parent material for the soils which developed under rapidly improving climatic conditions in post-glacial Britain. The evidence for this phase of the post-glacial environment is still present in many soil profiles on Exmoor, such as at Burcombe and sections exposed along the track between Pinkworthy Pond and Pinkery Farm. It is manifest in distinct subsoil stone lines, concentrations of stones in pockets and involutions typical of the formations produced under frozen ground conditions.

Increased chemical weathering and the development of a vegetation cover led to the establishment of predominantly mixed deciduous forest throughout the entire area. Soils, characteristically, would have comprised a brown topsoil associated either with a well-drained brown earth profile or else a gleyed brown earth in wetter hollows. The forest cover and soils were probably thinner on the exposed plateau surfaces and steeper slopes, in some cases comprising only thin mineral soils called 'rankers'.

There is a temptation to assume that soils may have been much more uniform in prehistoric times under the more or less continuous forest cover as a result of the pollen analytical evidence from a wide range of upland sites (Dimbleby, 1962). In truth we have little idea of the precise prehistoric pattern of soils and vegetation. Evidence from Bodmin Moor (Maltby & Caseldine, 1982) as well as earlier from the North York Moors (Dimbleby, 1962) certainly confirms that there may have been significant variation associated with differences in relief and parent material.

Little pollen will have been preserved in mineral soils until the profiles became either sufficiently acid and/or anaerobic to retard oxidation. Thus much of the early detail of soil and vegetation characteristics probably has been lost. However, the present dominance of acid peats with thin iron pan stagnopodzols and stagnohumic gleys on the upland surfaces and associated valley slopes are ecologically incongruous, with the mixed deciduous woodland vegetation indicated by such pollen evidence as exists.

Soil waterlogging, the development of peaty horizons, in some cases leading to the formation of blanket bog, progressive soil acidification, podzolidation and the formation of gley features occurred throughout the prehistoric period. These processes have been variously attributed to prehistoric human activity and the effects of climate change. The precise mechanisms involved and the relative importance of human and environmental factors are the subject of considerable and continued debate.

Evidence from Exmoor, however, has established a number of important findings:

1. Peat development did not begin at the same time over the whole upland area. On The Chains two millennia may have passed between the onset of peat development on the plateau surface and the growth of shallow deposits of peat on the marginal slopes.

2. Only thin mineral soil horizons are present beneath the deep peat whilst the thin peats are underlain by well-developed podzol or gley soil profiles.

3. The location of a flint artefact in relation to the horizon of a thin iron pan soil at Red Deer (SS 808396) is significant. It was found at 41-45 cm in the Bs horizon beneath 18 cm of peat and a thoroughly indurated iron pan (28 - 31 cm). The struck flake predates the development of these pedogenic features, since movement through them would be impossible without considerable and obvious disturbance of the profile for which there is no evidence. Crabtree and Maltby (1974) used pollen evidence to give a late Neolithic or Bronze Age date for deposition of the flake. This would indicate the absence of strongly podzolised soils or of an acid peat surface at Red Deer and probably throughout the flanks of the upland surface at a time when peat development was already well underway on the summit area of The Chains. Incorporation to the depth observed would only have taken place as a result of soil animal, especially earthworm, activity causing progressive burial. The iron pan and peat layer could only have formed later.

4. More recent discovery of a worked stone hand axe in a similar profile location confirms the probable existence of a mineral soil sufficiently fertile to support earthworms and other soil animals which over time would lead to the burial of the artefacts. There must have been a relative high pH (> 5.5), abundant nutrients and a vegetation cover in which trees probably featured prominently. Whether forest clearance and associated human activities such as burning and intensification of livestock grazing were alone sufficient to induce the subsequent leaching, acidification, gleying and peat initiation is still arguable.

Another chapter in this volume details the sequence of palaeoenvironmental change, but the important conclusions from basic soil research on Exmoor are:

1. Major alterations in soil-forming conditions took place during the prehistoric period coincident with human occupation and utilisation of the upland landscape.

2. The general result was degradation of soil in terms of their ability to support woodland cover. However, the loss of chemical fertility and increased waterlogging made it possible for acidophilous and hydrophytic plants to become established and led to the establishment of upland heath, moor and bog ecosystems.

3. The alteration in soil and ecosystem conditions would be consistent with increased leaching and paludification which could result from microclimate changes (leading to lower evapotranspiration loss and increased effective rainfall reaching the soil surface). The effects of such changes were probably concentrated in the Bronze Age for which there is abundant evidence of human monuments in the form of barrows, in the midst of the modern moorland. Examples such as The Chains Barrows and Five Barrows serve as a clear reminder that the landscape we now cherish may, in reality, have been the result of the first major human land-use disaster.

Whilst prehistory set the general conditions of modification of the upland landscape the historic period has been responsible for the development of the detailed patterns of the modern soils and vegetation. Probably from as early as Saxon times a large part of central Exmoor was protected under Forest Law and was used almost exclusively for the summer agistment of sheep and cattle (MacDermot, 1911). Under this land use regime, vegetation dominated by Molinia careulea and Trichophorum caespitosum developed over considerable parts of the Royal Forest, the limits of which become confirmed under the Norman and subsequent administrations. The term 'forest' does not refer to the existence of woodland but to a legal entity retained by the Crown largely for hunting and revenue purposes. Designation of the Royal Forest is responsible at least in places for contrasts in both vegetation and soil. In particular, a sharp boundary between the Molinia dominated association and one dominated by Calluna vulgaris occurs across the northern limit of the Exmoor Forest parish boundary. It occurs in places despite homogeneity in parent material and in the absence of significant geomorphological features. Precise accordance with the former Royal Forest boundary points to a remarkable man-made element in the present-day vegetation pattern. Written records provide only limited insight into the likely scale of landscape change resulting from establishment of the forest. Historical accounts of the vegetation are somewhat contradictory. MacDermot (1911) reports the observation in 1641 that 'in the greater part of the forest the pasture is sedge or coarse grass'. This would be a fair assessment of the current situation on The Chains and on the Morte Slates. However, a survey of Exmoor Chase in 1651 states 'but a verrye great part thereof is overgrowne with heath' (MacDermot, 1911). Whilst there are relatively few mature heather plants on The Chains there is a frequent presence of young growth and it is quite likely that the detailed pattern of dominance of the upland vegetation varied both in time and space according to management influences.

It is well-known that Calluna will not survive heavy grazing pressure and prefers relatively well drained soil conditions. Records indicate that at the end of the sixteenth century, 40,000 sheep, 1000 cattle and 400 horses were pastured annually in the forest and eighteenth century estimates continue to put the figure for sheep in excess of 30,000. Such intensive grazing pressure on an area of some 20,000 acres may have been an important factor in differentiating the more grazing-tolerant Molinia which dominated the central moor from the more carefully managed commons to the north and south. The deciduous character of the Molinia makes the community a good potential peat-former and establishment on the central moor may have been an important factor favouring the development of soils with a distinct peaty top or at least maintaining the peat of the blanket mire. The pattern of peat accumulation over time on The Chains has varied considerably (Figure 9). Throughout the period of administration as a Royal Forest the rate of peat growth was slow with heavy grazing pressure, regular burning and the manuring effect of animals stimulating decomposition rather than build up of litter. With

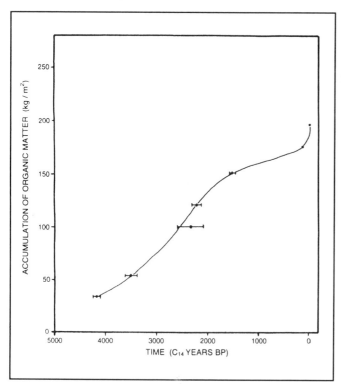

Figure 9 Accumulation of dry organic matter on The Chains blanket bog based on measurements by chemical oxidation. Levels of uncertainty associated with C₁₄ dates shown by horizontal lines.

nineteenth century enclosure the level of grazing on the open moor declined giving rise to an upsurge in the rate of accumulation – a dramatic illustration of the importance of land use regime on the ecological dynamics not only of vegetation but also peat formation. But the blanket bog on The Chains had certainly originated much earlier.

CHANGES IN THE NINETEENTH AND TWENTIETH CENTURIES

The Royal Forest was subject to enclosure in 1818. Under the direction of John Knight who purchased a large block of the original forest, and later his son Frederic Knight, reclamation of moorland for agriculture began to change land and landscape

on Exmoor. The operations and results of reclamation on the soil and vegetation have been recorded by Orwin & Sellick (1970), Curtis (1971), Maltby and Crabtree (1976) and Maltby (1977).

Detailed investigation of the effects of reclamation have provided a unique insight into the nature and speed of soil change. The salient aspects provide an important understanding of the extent to which upland soils can be manipulated by human actions.

Reclamation of moorland for agriculture was initiated soon after purchase of much of the area by John Knight who eventually bought 80% of the original Royal Forest (Orwin and Sellick, 1970). Nineteenth century operations concentrated on south-facing slopes and generally comprised of (i) paring off 50-75 mm of turf; (ii) burning the dried turf; (iii) spreading the ashes; (iv) ploughing – frequently 'half-ploughing'; (v) application of lime and slag; and (vi) re-seeding. The various techniques and management procedures associated with reclamation are well documented by Orwin and Sellick (1970). Twentieth century improvements omitted treatments (i) to (iii) but invariably included the addition of artificial nitrogenous fertilisers. Some schemes in the 1970s substituted herbicidal treatment, rotovating and direct drilling for ploughing (Horne, 1979).

Whilst originally varied mixtures were used for re-seeding (including Holcus lanatus, Cynosaurus cristatus, Dactylis glomerata and Phleum pratense) the most recent schemes concentrated on rye-grass and clover varieties.

The generalised distribution of soils on south-facing slopes is shown in Figure 10. Stagnopodzols and stagnohumic gleys frequently occur in close association giving a complex pattern of profile forms on sub-summit slopes. Reclamation over the last 150 years has been directed in particular towards the improvement and modification of these soils and associated moorland vegetation on the gentle gradients of the valley shoulder and lower crest slopes ideally suited to mechanical operations. Of particular significance is the fact that sites can be found on Exmoor which differ in time since reclamation was initiated between the nineteenth century and the 1970s.

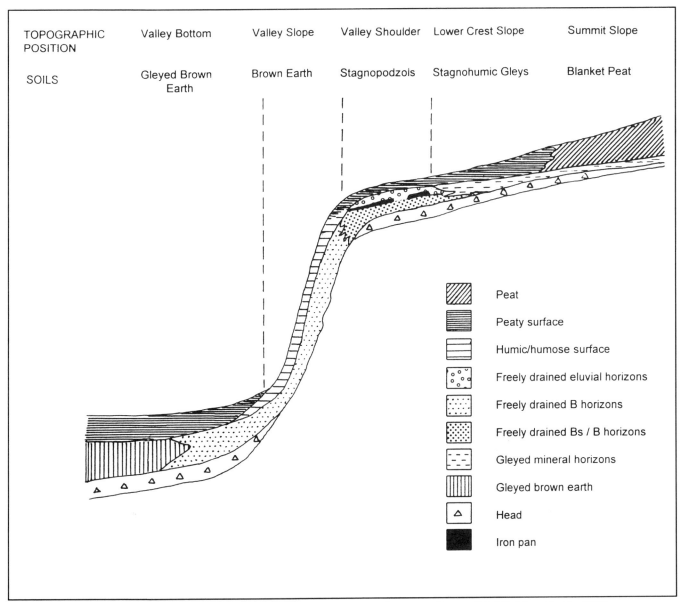

TOPOGRAPHIC POSITION	Valley Bottom	Valley Slope	Valley Shoulder	Lower Crest Slope	Summit Slope
SOILS	Gleyed Brown Earth	Brown Earth	Stagnopodzols	Stagnohumic Gleys	Blanket Peat

Legend:
- Peat
- Peaty surface
- Humic/humose surface
- Freely drained eluvial horizons
- Freely drained B horizons
- Freely drained Bs / B horizons
- Gleyed mineral horizons
- Gleyed brown earth
- Head
- Iron pan

Figure 10 Generalised distribution of soils on south-facing slopes in Exmoor Forest. (Modified from Curtis, 1971).

37

Research has focused on the nature and speed of change in two important soil profile types (a) a stagnohumic gley (Wilsey series), and (b) a stagnohumic gley (Hiraithrog series).

Detailed investigations including morphological, chemical and microbiological analyses have revealed a number of key findings which have been documented by Maltby, (1975, 1977, 1984 and 1989).

A new surface A horizon (epipedon) with diagnostic brown earth characteristics can be formed from the original acidic peaty surface, together with variable incorporations of underlying mineral horizons (such as E, Eg, Ag, Bs or Bg) of the thin iron pan stagnopodzol and stagnohumic gley, in less than 130 years. The A horizon has no genetic relationship with the surviving sub-soil horizons of the original moorland soil profile but is the result of the immediate morphological effects of reclamation together with the new soil-forming conditions maintained by vegetation change and intensified land use.

The mechanical processes of reclamation can produce a coarse mixing effect of organic and inorganic soil horizons and also bring about chemical changes due to improved aeration; but the development of the new A horizon depends on the sustained biological activity of earthworms and micro-organisms. Significant populations of earthworms may become established only after a number of years but large increases in microbial numbers occur within days of reclamation. If suitable conditions of soil pH, nutrient status, drainage and plant litter are not maintained for a sufficient length of time biological 'take-off' may not occur and the well-mixed brown earth type A horizon will not develop. However, once take-off has been achieved the process of soil development may be self-sustaining. The rate of change of the underlying podzol or gley subsoil horizons is significantly slower than that of the A horizon and a significant area of future enquiry should be able to evaluate the speed at which these horizons are altered.

Deterioration of the grazing quality of the vegetation and reduced management enables moorland species to re-establish. Such 'reversion' is associated with the re-accumulation of surface organic matter in the soil profile which may lead eventually to the redevelopment of a peaty horizon.

The rate of re-accumulation of organic matter is much slower than either its rate of loss due to agricultural improvement or the rate of fixation in the original moorland soil profile (Table 1).

Peaty surface horizons intact moorland stagnohumic gley – thin iron pan podzol mosaic (1833 - 1974)	+ 0.6 - 1.0
Reclaimed stagnohumic gley – thin iron pan stagnopodzol profiles (1845 - 1982)	- 0.6
Reverted stagnohumic gley – thin iron pan stagnopodzol profile (1847 - 1982)	+ 0.1
After Maltby, 1985	

Table 1 Gain/loss organic carbon t/ha/yr under different soil/land conditions, Exmoor.

This reflects the significant extent of human disturbance of the soil-forming environment and the inevitable delay in any recovery rate matching either the pre-disturbance rate of organic carbon fixation or the rate of oxidation loss due to altered drainage, pH nutrient and biological conditions.

Many of the previously improved pastures on Exmoor demonstrate mosaics of vegetation reflecting various degrees of reversion. Stock tend not to graze the reverted vegetation as intensively so allowing more litter to accumulate. Accumulation is facilitated by the aged nature of the plant material and the reduced manuring effect of livestock. Over a distance of just several metres it is possible to observe patches of less intensively grazed sward with an accumulating litter/organic horizon amidst areas of more intensively grazed sward maintaining a brown earth type of horizon. This highlights the sensitivity of soil profile response to the subtle interactions of vegetation on grazing animals and underlines the significance of human intervention.

PINKERY CANAL - AN ENVIRONMENTALLY SIGNIFICANT FEATURE

Much of what we know about the rate of recent soil change and the precise role of human intervention in directing a new course of pedogenesis on upland Exmoor is underpinned by the preservation of the original pre-nineteenth century reclamation moorland profile under the spoil of the Pinkery Canal. This 'water carriageway' which contours the southern slopes of The Chains from close to Pinkworthy Ford (SS924423) to Exe Head (SS752413) was constructed in 1833 (Crabtree and Maltby, 1974).

It predates the designation of Pinkery Farm by some 12 years and the reclamation of the enclosed moorland by at least 15 years. The typical double stone walls with the centre space filled with earth and planted with beech trees cut across the canal, thus confirming its earlier date.

Along the length of the canal the spoil has sealed the original thin iron pan stagnopodzol and stagnohumic gley and various intergrade profiles. Much of the adjacent land on the southern flanks of The Chains has been reclaimed for improved agriculture at various times since the mid-nineteenth century and the soils show substantially modified A horizon characteristics.

The canal provides the soil and environmental scientist with a unique tool, confirming precisely the earlier existence at the reclaimed sites of the podzol and gleyed profile still extant in the remaining intact moorland. It enables valid spatially separate comparisons to be made between reclaimed, unreclaimed and reverted soil conditions and differences interpreted as a response to temporal change.

The context of the canal and the recorded land use changes which have occurred in adjacent areas provide one of the most important outdoor laboratory sites for the investigation of the influence of human actions on upland pedogenesis certainly in Britain and probably anywhere in Europe. It is important that this value is recognised fully by the National Park Authority and that appropriate actions should be taken to ensure survival and best use of the scientific sites and the evidence they have yielded and might generate in the future.

RELEVANCE TO THEORY OF SOIL CHANGE AND DEVELOPMENT

In 1953 Crompton published a paper entitled '*Grow the grass to grow the soil*' in which he referred to the possibilities of upland soils developing either peaty, moor surface horizons in association with coarse, acidophilous little grazed moorland vegetation or brown earth-like mull horizons in association with improved more heavily grazed agricultural swards. The Exmoor story provides the scientific evidence which adds time-scales, pedogenic and soil ecological detail to this theory. It is clear that the upland soil-forming environment offers a range of possibilities and the point of soil-steady state which might be attainable is variable and directly dependent on human intervention. The proximate controls on soil morphology are internal to the soil profile and determined in particular by biological activity in the surface horizons. Factors of drainage, acidity, litter quality and nutrient status exert major controls over biological activity. All of these factors are liable to land management changes. We can regard the moorland soil profile as 'poised' and capable of being changed fundamentally by even subtle changes in the balance of soil forming factors.

The scale and intensity of soil changes by human intervention was formulated into a simple process-response model by Yaalon and Yaron (1966). They described human induced soil change as 'metapedogenesis' and distinguished this from 'natural' pedogenesis by the greater speed and possible reversibility of soil development. Both of these factors are characteristic of the reclaimed profiles on Exmoor.

Maltby (1977) introduced the term 'palingenesis' (literally 'born again') to describe soil profiles which assumed the character of an earlier cycle or period of development. We can extend this idea to describe the status of individual horizons. Thus, the formation of a brown earth type A horizon can be regarded as palingenetic in relation to an original mineral soil associated with the prehistoric forest vegetation. Reclamation within the last 150 years has turned back the clock of soil development by perhaps 3000 years and without the essential assistance of climatic change. The fact that the soil profile can change so readily justifies a healthy scepticism of the need to infer climate as the primary factor determining alteration of the soil-forming environment and subsequent soil development.

APPLICATION TO MODERN MOORLAND MANAGEMENT

The experience from investigations of the historical change in soil and vegetation can be applied to the improved understanding of potential landscape modification resulting from further human activity or environmental change. Such knowledge can be used perhaps even more importantly to actually engineer change including the restoration of soil and vegetation to particularly desirable conditions. Past research has focused on the scientific assessment of experimental manipulations of land management. This has been carried out in direct collaboration with Exmoor National Park and has been possible in conjunction with various management agreements with landowners (Curtis and Maltby, 1980).

A principle aim of the early land management agreements was to achieve an enhancement of grazing quality of intact moorland vegetation without so changing plant community and/or soil characteristics that would lead to loss of the moorland habitat. Thus application of lime and slag was permitted to patches of already unimproved vegetation but not ploughing or re-seeding operations, and adjacent areas of heather or Molinia moorland were to remain untreated. Some areas of moorland were fenced off to serve as long-term controls against observed changes. The results of monitoring for the last 15 years give rise to a number of important concerns surrounding the use of partial land improvement solutions for moorland management:

1. Rapid loss of heather occurs in areas adjacent to those surface treated (2 t lime and 0.5 t slag per acre). This can take place within just several years and is probably the result of increased grazing pressure since fenced enclosures retain vigorous heather growth.

2. Significant increases in microbiological activity results from surface treatment. This is both immediate, due to pH and nutrient changes, as well as delayed in response to changes in litter quality and the decomposition cycle (Figure 11).

3. Improvement in soil condition in terms of elevated pH, nutrient status and microbiological activity is sustained for a period of at least 8 years after treatment, and probably for a decade or more. Whilst it is unclear whether a single treatment is sufficient to sustain progressive soil change it is clear that treatments on a 10 - 15 year cycle might promote fundamental alteration of acid, peaty-topped soils. The result will be much more biologically-active profiles with mull, brown earth-like topsoils supporting not acidic grassland or heathers but 'improved' grass swards dominated by species Agrostis, Festuca, Lolium, Poa, Trifolium and a wide range of herbs. Such swards are favoured and to a significant extent are maintained by grazing.

THOUGHTS ON FUTURE DIRECTIONS FOR THE UPLAND LANDSCAPE

Conservation of habitats or landscape should not be equated with preservation or the fossilisation of a particular pattern. If this had been so in prehistory we would not have the extensive vistas of particular moorland ecosystems today. Change is a natural feature of the natural environment and even systems in so called equilibrium undergo dynamic oscillations about some average condition. Conservation is about managing change and in particular preventing high speed change which is normally deleterious for survival of nature populations and ecosystem conditions.

Management is the fundamental control of the landscape detail in Exmoor. It influences not only vegetation but also the course of soil development. Thus it is by human actions that the most effective conservation results will be attained. The delivery of suitable management actions depends on at least two conditions being met:

i. A reliable scientific understanding of the nature and rate of change due to particular actions.

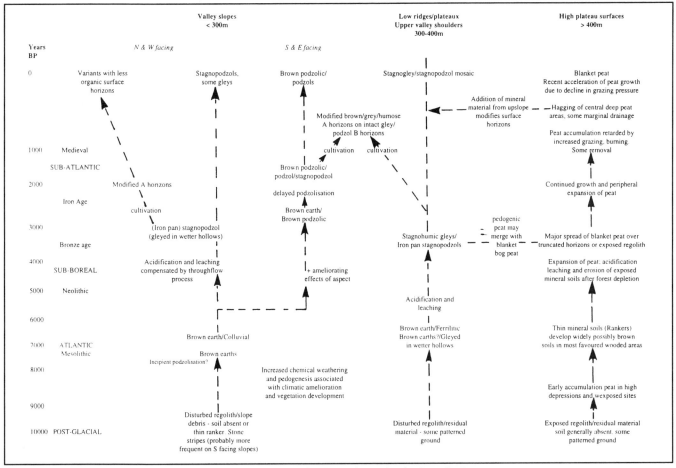

Figure 11 Outline of soil transformation in the uplands.

ii. A verifiable and affordable means of implementation of management prescriptions.

The solution to (i) will be met by the further development of partnerships and collaboration among scientists, landowners and the Exmoor National Park. There are still many questions which need answers such as what is the most effective means of accelerating reversion; what are the maximum stocking rates which maintain a heather/grass mosaic; how and at what rate can soil pH and base status be reduced in formerly reclaimed areas and can peat development be re-established?

In the case of (ii) the solutions are much more complex. The basic requirement is funding and this will be realised by responsible agencies such as the Exmoor National Park, DOE and MAFF arguing the case for finance. Given the inevitable limitations to the funding base it is essential that the wisest investments are made in the management of the upland landscape. The overall balance of moorland and agricultural land is now relatively stable, but the opportunity exists for redressing the recent historic shift and increasing the area of open moorland habitat. Science can provide the necessary support to target strategic and cost-effective changes but society, government and landowners must decide with the responsible agencies whether it is the status quo or some other pattern which is the desired landscape objective. The scientific options are exciting, the socio-economic implications challenging and the wider human dimensions daunting. Yet what we decide now sets the standards for the following generations. What is important is that there are possibilities for choice.

REFERENCES

K. Crabtree and E. Maltby, 'Soil and land use change on Exmoor. Significance of a buried profile on Exmoor', *Somerset Archaeology and Natural History*, 119, (1974).

E. Crompton, 'Grow the soil to grow the grass. Some pedological aspects of marginal land improvement', *Agriculture*, 60, (1953) 301-308.

L.F. Curtis, 'Soils of Exmoor Forest', *Soil Survey of Great Britain Special Survey*, No.5, (1971) 77.

L.F. Curtis. and E. Maltby, 'Conserve or Concede – How best to strike the balance of use in Britain's smallest National Park – Exmoor', *Farmers Weekly*, 27 June 1980.

G.W. Dimbleby, 'The development of British Heathlands and their soils', *Oxford Forestry Mem.*, No.23, (1962).

T.C.B. Horne, 'Reclamation on Exmoor', *Welsh Soils Discussion Group Rep*, No. 20, (1979).

E.T. MacDermot, *The History of the Forest of Exmoor*, (Taunton 1911).

E. Maltby, 'Numbers of soils micro-organisms as ecological indicators of changes resulting from moorland reclamation on Exmoor', *J. Biogeogr.* 2, (1975) 117-136.

E. Maltby, 'Ecological indicators of changes in soil conditions resulting from moorland reclamation on Exmoor', (unpublished. PhD thesis, University of Bristol,1977).

E. Maltby, 'Changes in soil properties and vegetation resulting from reclamation on Exmoor', *Welsh Soils Discussion Group Rep.* No. 20, (1979) 83-117.

E. Maltby, 'Response of soil microflora to moorland reclamation for improved agriculture', *Plant and Soil*, 76, (1984) 183-193.

E. Maltby, 'Investigation of differential trends in upland soil development resulting from reclamation of moorland for agriculture', *Final report to NERC.*, (1985).

E. Maltby, 'Development, agricultural conversion and environmental investigations of wet soils and peat', in E. Maltby and T. Wollerson, eds., *Soils and their Management: a Sino-European Perspective* (1989).

E. Maltby and C.J. Caseldine, 'Prehistoric soil and vegetation development on Bodmin Moor, southwestern England', *Nature*, 297, (1982) 397-400.

E. Maltby and K. Crabtree, 'Soil organic matter and peat accumulation on Exmoor: a contemporary and palaeo-environmental evaluation', *Trans. Inst. Brit. Geog.*, 1 (3), (1976) 259-278.

D.L. Merryfield and P.D. Moore, 'Prehistoric human activity and blanket peat initiation on Exmoor', *Nature*, Lond., 250, (1974) 439-441.

C.S. Orwin and R.J. Sellick, *The Reclamation of Exmoor Forest*, 2nd edition, (Newton Abbot, 1970).

D. Yaalon and B. Yaron, 'Framework for man-made soil changes – an outline of metapedogenesis', *Soil Sci.*, 102, (1966) 272-277.

PALAEOENVIRONMENTAL STUDIES ON EXMOOR: PAST RESEARCH AND FUTURE POTENTIAL

Vanessa Straker and Keith Crabtree
Department of Geography, University of Bristol

INTRODUCTION: THE POTENTIAL OF PALAEOENVIRONMENTAL STUDIES

Palaeoenvironmental studies, the analysis of the remains of plants and animals which survive in ancient sediments, and the sediments themselves, provide us with a picture of how the landscape has changed and are now a standard and important part of archaeological projects

The variety of biological material that can be preserved is very wide, ranging in scale from whole animal skeletons to pollen grains of only 20 microns in diameter. It is desirable to be able to study several different types of material, as an integrated approach often provides us with the best evidence for reconstruction of past environments and land use. However, survival of plant and animal remains is governed largely by the nature of the sediments in which they become trapped. Animal bones, snails, and other organisms composed largely of calcium carbonate are not preserved in acid soils, whereas pollen grains are poorly preserved in dry, biologically active soils. The remains of larger parts of plants such as fruits, seeds, and wood often survive in deposits that are waterlogged. In dry soils they are usually only preserved as charred fragments surviving from fires that have turned them to charcoal rather than burning them away completely. The exoskeletal remains of insects, which are of increasing importance to the study of past environments, survive best in waterlogged deposits.

On Exmoor, the geology, soils and climate give rise to largely acid conditions and the study of soils and sediments, pollen, plant macrofossils and, possibly, insect remains offers the greatest potential for the future. In the past, archaeobotanical analysis has concentrated on the technique of pollen analysis and it is the results of some of this work which has been carried out by Merryfield, Moore, Crabtree, Francis and Slater that will be summarised in this paper.

DEVELOPMENT OF THE LANDSCAPE: THE EVIDENCE FROM POLLEN ANALYSIS

Pollen accumulates in sediments as they are laid down and is often very well preserved in mires. Much of the higher part of Exmoor is covered with blanket mire (peat) and peat has also accumulated in valleys and ground water seepage sites. The Exmoor coast also has considerable potential for environmental reconstruction, a good example being the intertidal peat in Porlock Bay which is associated with remains of former woodland.

There is also a wealth of potential information, at present untapped, from deposits which are directly associated with archaeological sites. These include soils buried beneath barrows or boundary walls and other contexts such as the fills of pits and ditches and occupation layers in houses. They are important because they give us specific information about the

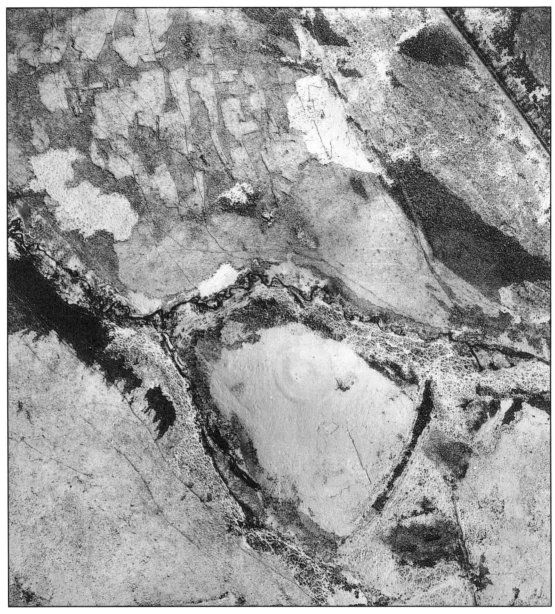

Plate 18 Porlock Allotment (SS 841436) from the air, showing hut platform within enclosure and examples of the effect of peat cutting.

landscape in which a particular settlement developed and how it may have exploited or been adapted to the surrounding landscape. This 'local' detail enhances the picture painted by pollen analysis of peat which provides the regional setting. The size of the peat bog affects the catchment of the pollen and small bogs tend to reflect more local vegetation than very large ones. One other advantage of peat is that it can be radiocarbon-dated so that the pollen analyst can look at the changes in the vegetation that have taken place by comparing, for example, how the tree cover has changed over the last few thousand years with the behaviour of other types of plant community such as grassland and heathland, and date the particular levels at which the changes are noted.

BLANKET MIRE

Merryfield (1977) as part of his postgraduate research, estimated that there were under 8000 hectares of peat more than 10 cm in depth on Exmoor and that this formed a discontinuous blanket which was most extensive in the north. This is a much smaller area than on other comparable uplands such as Dartmoor, parts of Wales and the Pennines, and he concluded that its distribution was affected by altitude, bedrock, climate and human activity. Most of the peat is on land of over 305 m in altitude but not all of the land of this height and above is peat covered. Deep peat also forms in valleys, as well as the broad flat summits, that near Pinkworthy Pond being recorded as over 2 m deep. However, most of Exmoor's peat is less than 30 cm deep (Merryfield 1977).

Since Merryfield's work was completed, an archaeological survey by McDonnell (pers. comm.) has provided direct evidence of how extensive peat cutting for fuel has been in the past, and it is possible that in places peat may have been completely removed (Plate 18). The deepest peat that survives is on The Chains and was first studied by Merryfield (1977) and the pollen analyses published by Merryfield and Moore (1974) and Moore, Merryfield, and Price (1984).

Pollen analysis on The Chains has also been carried out by Crabtree and is summarised below. The radiocarbon dates that are quoted are those published by Merryfield, Moore, Price,

Francis and Slater (above), but the calibrations to 2 sigma (95% confidence) that are used in this paper were provided by Alex Bayliss (Ancient Monuments Laboratory, English Heritage[1]). Moore (1993) and others have discussed the possible factors involved in the development of blanket peat on Britain's uplands. The following factors have been suggested:

1. Altitude, as temperature and exposure affect the growth and decay of bog plants.
2. Climatic humidity resulting in low rates of evaporation.
3. Topography.
4. Tree clearance reducing interception, transpiration and resulting in waterlogging of the soil.
5. The use of fire to clear vegetation which may have prevented recovery of woodland.
6. Acidification resulting in podzolisation reducing earthworm activity, promoting iron pan formation and altering the drainage. The growth of *Calluna* (ling) can accelerate iron pan formation.

Localised factors may result in peat formation for a variety of reasons at different dates, as the table below shows for Exmoor. Peat depth is related to site factors, vegetation, the rate of vegetation breakdown and compaction. Thus, peat accumulates at different rates and peat depth is no guide to age.

SITE	ALTITUDE (M)	PEAT DEPTH (CM)	LAB CODE	DATE OF PEAT INCEPTION
HOAR TOR	416	107		?550 - 50 BC[2]
HOAR MOOR	433	108	I-15,549	5410 ± 110 BP 4470 - 4000 cal 2s BC
CODSEND MOORS	461	90	I-16,087	2270±150 BP cal 2s BC 800 - 20 AD
CHAINS	488	281		c. 3075 BC[2]

Table 2 Peat formation on Exmoor.

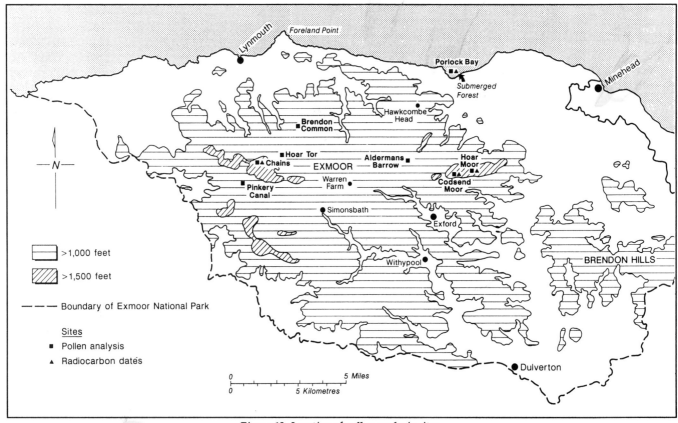

Figure 12 Location of pollen analysis sites.

Figure 12 shows the location of sites where pollen analysis has been carried out at The Chains, Hoar Tor, Brendon Common and Alderman's Barrow (Merryfield 1977; Merryfield and Moore 1974, Moore *et al.* 1984) and Hoar Moor and Codsend Moors (Francis and Slater 1990, 1992). The sampling locations were not directly associated with archaeological sites, though The Chains and Alderman's Barrow sites are near to the barrows. The Codsend and Hoar Moor profiles were about 400 m from a prehistoric field system and field walls can be seen running into blanket peat. At Codsend, the basal date of 2270±150 BP suggests that the adjacent field system must pre-date this.

Two of these studies will be summarised below. The following account is a case study summarising the results of a previously unpublished analysis by K. Crabtree from the Chains. The data are presented in Figure 13.

The Chains is at present covered by unreclaimed blanket peat up to 3 m deep supporting a vegetation of *Molinia caerulea* (purple moor grass), *Eriorophorum* spp.(cotton grass), *Calluna* (ling), and *Sphagnum* spp.(bog mosses). Merryfield and Moore (1974) and Moore *et al.* (1984) provide a partial pollen diagram with radiocarbon dates from a profile of 285 cm depth. The earliest radiocarbon date at 240 cm was 4170±75BP (UB-821),

Colour Plate 1 *Porlock Bay and Marsh.*

Colour Plate 2 *Coring peat at Hoar Moor using a Russian borer to obtain samples for pollen analysis.*

Colour Plate 3 *Heddon's Mouth.*

Colour Plate 4 *Dulverton Silk Mill (now the Laundry). (Courtesy Brian Pearce).*

although Moore *et al.* consider the whole profile to go back to about 3000 BC. This basal date calibrates to 2920 - 2500 BC at 2s, lending support to their interpretation.

Figure 13 is a pollen diagram, also from The Chains, about 100 m to the south of the Merryfield and Moore site, 50 m north of The Chains Barrow. In this diagram, the lowest organic accumulation (CB1, 247-260 cm) has tree and shrub pollen in excess of 50% TLP (total land pollen). This suggests that closed woodland was present at or adjacent to the site. The woodland was composed largely of oak and alder with hazel or bog myrtle. (It is very difficult to differentiate the pollen of these last two shrubs). Some open vegetation was present locally, largely represented by grass and sedge. Heathland with *Calluna* (ling or heather) became increasingly important and as *Calluna* is insect pollinated, the high pollen values must represent the local growth of heather.

From 247-217 cm (CB2) herbaceous pollen values exceed 50% TLP, but the absence of clearance indicators such as *Plantago lanceolata* (ribwort plantain) and *Pteridium* (bracken) and the dominance of grass, sedge and heather pollen suggest that the increasingly open vegetation was due to the initial spread of blanket peat rather than active clearance by humans. Nevertheless, Merryfield and Moore did relate this change, noted in their diagram and radiocarbon dated to 4170±75 BP (UB-821), to possible human interference.

At 215 cm, a sudden change is apparent with a rise in ribwort plantain pollen and bracken spores. By 210 cm the herbaceous pollen total is over 60% TLP. It is suggested that this represents a period of active clearance in the adjacent woodland areas.

At 185 cm a further big increase in these open ground indicators occurs, together with further falls in the total tree pollen values, supporting a view of intensified clearance. The magnitude of the changes suggests a correlation with Merryfield and Moore's assemblage zone ChE the base of which is radiocarbon dated to 2335±260 BP. At two sigma this calibrates to 1010 BC - 220 AD and could therefore be late Bronze Age, Iron Age or even early Roman. However, the date for the middle part of this zone is more useful (UB-817 2215±90

BP) and calibrates at two sigma to 410-50 BC, the later Iron Age. Heather pollen decreases at this time, while sedge pollen increases markedly. The peat is dominated by the coarse fibres of cotton grass. This pollen change must be due to acid grassland development with cotton grass as a major constituent of the local on-site vegetation.

At 140 cm there are signs of some decrease in the ruderal species and an increase in tree pollen, indicating a possible recession in the agricultural activity in the vicinity, but by 100cm *Gramineae*, *Ericaceae* (heathers) and some of the ruderals rise again and retain high values in the few samples analysed in the upper metre. The rise in *Pinus* (pine) at 20 cm was suggested by Merryfield and Moore to be dated to the period of the Napoleonic wars or to eighteenth century plantings, but Crabtree and Maltby (1976) on the basis of documentary and buried soil evidence suggest a more recent date, probably post 1840.

A summary of the vegetation changes identified at Hoar Moor, the other long radiocarbon-dated sequence for Exmoor, adapted from Francis and Slater (1990) is presented in Table 3 on page 50.

It is clear from these studies that tree cover existed on Exmoor before the blanket peat developed on the broad summits and may well have continued for longer on steep slopes and in valleys. The basal peat on The Chains overlies a mineral soil providing evidence of the former woodland cover with oak well represented as well as hazel, birch, pine, alder, elm and lime (Moore *et al.* 1984). Pollen from the soil was not studied at Hoar Moor (Francis and Slater 1990), but at the base of the peat in Zone HM A 1 *c* 80% tree and shrub pollen was recorded.

At Warren Farm, at an altitude of 420 m, direct evidence for the former woodland cover is provided by the presence of tree stumps preserved beneath the peat (McDonnell 1985). At both The Chains (Merryfield and Moore 1974) and Hoar Moor, an elm decline is noted in the mid fourth millennium BC, and this event, now thought to be possibly connected to an outbreak of elm disease rather than the activity of humans alone, is often poorly recognised in the South West. Disease apart, why trees

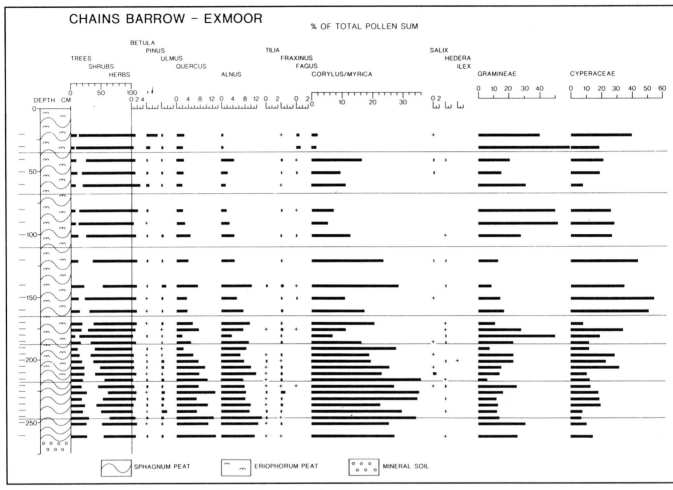

CHAINS BARROW - EXMOOR

% OF TOTAL POLLEN SUM

Figure 13a and b Pollen diagram from The Chains.

48

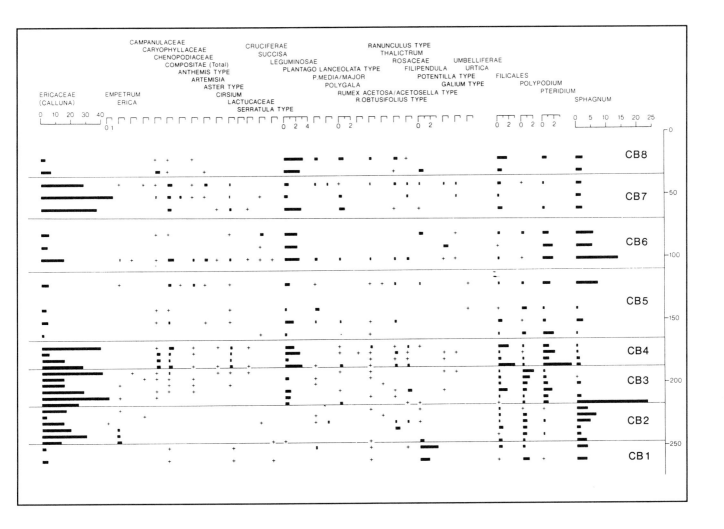

CAMPANULACEAE
CARYOPHYLLACEAE
CHENOPODIACEAE
COMPOSITAE (Total)
ANTHEMIS TYPE
ARTEMISIA
ASTER TYPE
CIRSIUM
LACTUCACEAE
SERRATULA TYPE
CRUCIFERAE
SUCCISA
LEGUMINOSAE
PLANTAGO LANCEOLATA TYPE
P.MEDIA/MAJOR
POLYGALA
RUMEX ACETOSA/ACETOSELLA TYPE
R.OBTUSIFOLIUS TYPE
RANUNCULUS TYPE
THALICTRUM
ROSACEAE
FILIPENDULA
POTENTILLA TYPE
GALIUM TYPE
UMBELLIFERAE
URTICA
FILICALES
POLYPODIUM
PTERIDIUM
SPHAGNUM

ERICACEAE
(CALLUNA)
EMPETRUM
ERICA

0 10 20 30 40
0 1
0 2 4
0 2
0 2
0 2 0 2 0 2
0 5 10 15 20 25
0

CB8

50
CB7

CB6
100

CB5

150

CB4
200
CB3

CB2
250
CB1

49

ZONE	RADIOCARBON DATES FOR PEAT AT BASE OF ZONE	VEGETATION
HM A 8	240±80 BP (I-15,546) AD 1460 - 1955 (cal, 2s)	Modest increase in trees in an open, grass dominated landscape. Increase in pine due to plantations?
HM A 6-7	380±80 BP (I-15,547) AD 1410 - 1660 (cal 2s)	Lowest tree and shrub cover. Phases of grassland and then heather domination, especially the latter at the top of the zone.
HM A 5		Slight increase in trees and shrubs, but grassland dominates. Many sedges, possibly arable nearby.
HM A 4		Main rise in heathers. Charcoal layers suggesting burning and possibly grazing. Fluctuations between heather and grass dominated moorland.
HM A 3	1760±80 BP (I-15,548) AD 80 -430 (cal, 2 s)	Trees and shrubs continue to decrease, but beech is recorded. Heathers start to rise. Increase in *Rumex* (sorrels) and plantains suggesting disturbance. Locally wet – *Sphagnum* and sedges may suggest increasingly acid conditions.
HM A 2		Locally wet – increase in alder and sedges. Opening up of landscape, increasing grassland (possibly pasture). Woodland clearance – lime disappears at about 1000 BC.
HM A 1	5410±110 BP (I-15,549) 4470 - 4000 BC (cal, 2s)	80% TLP is tree and shrub pollen: birch (particularly), and oak, hazel/bog myrtle, pine, alder, elm and lime.

Table 3 Vegetation changes at Hoar Moor.

were cleared is open to question, but plants such as *Potentilla* flourish when browsed or grazed and it is reasonable to suggest that open grazing for stock was required. They may also have browsed on accessible leaf fodder such as hazel, ash or lime.

The calculated dates for the onset of peat accumulation (see above) suggest that at the various sites it occurred at different times and that in some locations on Exmoor it may cover areas of prehistoric landscape. This can be seen at Codsend Moors where a field system survives, but disappears from view in places where it has been engulfed by blanket peat.

In order to be able to respond to proposals to alter land use and provide the background for management plans, further palaeoenvironmental research is needed. Firstly, an up-to-date plan of areas of peat cover and depth is required. Secondly, strategically-targeted pollen, plant macrofossil and possibly insect analyses, as well as being vital to the understanding of the landscape context of archaeological monuments, will also help to answer questions about the reduction of woodland cover and the nature of the development of heather moorland and *Molinia* grassland. These fluctuated in their cover dominance many times in the past probably as a result of land management and grazing pressure. The analyses will also allow us to address questions regarding the status of beech on Exmoor, so important a component of the hedges today, and planted as hedges by the Knight family. Beech does not appear in the Exmoor pollen diagrams until the late Roman period at the earliest but beech charcoal has been identified from archaeological sites in south-western England from about 3000 BC. It is possible that although it may not have been a component of the former woodland cover on the plateau tops, beech was part of the valley woodland.

These are but a few specific questions for which palaeo-environmental work may be able to provide solutions. That work itself is likely to raise further questions but at the same time provide a temporal and spatial framework for environmental change and human exploitation of the landscape.

REFERENCES

K. Crabtree and E. Maltby, 'Soil and Land Use Change on Exmoor: significance of a buried profile on Exmoor', *Proceedings of the Somerset Archaeological and Natural History Society*, 119, (1974) 38-43.

P.D. Francis and D.S. Slater, 'A record of vegetational and land use change from upland peat deposits on Exmoor. Part 2: Hoar Moor', *PSANS*, 134, (1990) 1-25.

P.D. Francis and D.S. Slater, 'A record of vegetational and land use change from upland peat deposits on Exmoor. Part 3: Codsend Moors', *PSANS*, 136, (1992) 9-28.

R. McDonnell, *Recommendations for the Management of Archaeological Sites in the Exmoor National Park at Warren, Pinford, Tom's Hill and Hayes Allotment*, Western Archaeological Trust (1985).

D.L. Merryfield, 'Palynological and stratigraphical studies on Exmoor', (unpublished PhD thesis, Kings College, London, 1977).

D.L. Merryfield and P.D. Moore, 'Prehistoric human activity and blanket peat initiation on Exmoor', *Nature* 250, (1974) 439-441.

P.D. Moore, D.L. Merryfield and M.D.R. Price, 'The Vegetation and Development of Blanket Mires', in P.D. Moore, ed., *European Mires*, (1984) 203-235.

P.D. Moore, 'The origin of blanket mire, revisited', in F. Chambers, ed., *Climatic Change and Human Impact on the Landscape*, (1993) 218-224.

G.W. Pearson, J.R. Pilcher, M.G.L. Baillie, D.M. Corbett and F. Qua, 'High precision C_{14} measurement of Irish oaks to show the natural C_{14} variation from AD 1840 - 5210 BC', *Radiocarbon* 28, (1986) 911-934.

G.W. Pearson and M. Stuiver, 'High precision calibration of the radiocarbon timescale, 500 - 2500 BC', *Radiocarbon* 28, (1986) 838-862.

M. Stuiver and G.W. Pearson, 'High precision calibration of the radiocarbon timescale, AD 1950 - 500 BC', *Radiocarbon* 28, (1986) 805-838.

M. Stuiver and P.J.Reimer, 'A computer programme for radiocarbon age calculations', *Radiocarbon* 28, (1986) 1022-1030.

ACKNOWLEDGEMENTS

We would like to thank David Merryfield for permission to quote from his PhD thesis; Richard McDonnell for supplying Plate 18 and Colour Plate 2 and Simon Godden who drew Figures 12 and 13. The RCHME gave permission for the use of Plate 18, NMR 1459/291 © Crown copyright.
We are very grateful to Alex Bayliss, Ancient Monuments Laboratory, English Heritage for providing the calibrations for the radiocarbon dates.

[1] Calibrations were made using the maximum intercept method of Stuiver and Reimer (1986) and data from Stuiver and Pearson (1986); Pearson and Stuiver (1986) and Pearson et al., (1986).

[2] The date for blanket mire inception at Hoar Tor is suggested by the correlation of the pollen spectrum with that from the radiocarbon-dated Chains profile, and the date for peat inception at The Chains relies on estimates of peat accumulation rates and a date of 4170±75 BP (UB-821) at 40 cm above the base of the profile (Moore et al., 1984).

INVESTIGATING AND INTERPRETING THE MAN-MADE EXMOOR LANDSCAPE

Veryan Heal

Archaeologist, Exmoor National Park Authority

Exmoor is not a wilderness, nor is it the product of natural processes alone. What we see is a man-made landscape. The rocks and soils of its geological foundations are overlain by historic features and secondary and seminatural ecology. These are the products of human clearance of postglacial forests in order to use the land and the timber, of man's early impoverishment of upland soils, of management of the secondary open and woodland habitats which developed as a result, and of more recent attempts to increase production by artificially improving the soil. Man has been changing the face of Exmoor for some 10,000 years.

Following the end of the last glaciation, the development of a temperate climate led to recolonisation of the land by flora and fauna such that the environment of Exmoor became more attractive to man. The development of differing ecological niches resulted in a range of flora and fauna which provided the resources essential for human existence: plants, animals and fish as foodstuffs and materials for construction, artefacts, shelter and clothing. As yet we know of no palaeolithic sites or finds from Exmoor, but mesolithic communities were present in the seventh millennium BC, taking advantage of the natural riches by hunting and gathering, as is shown by artefacts left at summer hunting camps on the hills and on the coast.

Subsequent technological developments during the Neolithic period, leading to the predominantly agricultural economy which persists today, extended the range and means of human exploitation. The role of man in the biosphere changed from that of a passive exploiter of natural resources to that of an active exploiter and transformer of his habitat, seeking to control and ensure production of necessary supplies.

The palimpsest of Exmoor's historic landscape can be examined and interpreted to explain how those processes of exploitation changed the immature face of postglacial Exmoor, providing features and texture, the 'wrinkles' of maturity, which give it much of its present character. Archaeology provides the main techniques used to investigate the historic environment, its purpose being to reveal the way of life of past communities through the physical remains left behind by their activities. It is not the study of odd things that have been found to be viewed simply as *objets d'art*. Archaeological survey and excavation seek to determine the form, purpose and origin of manmade features and their temporal and spatial relationships.

An essential adjunct to this is analysis of the palaeo-environment, the context in which the human activities which shaped the landscape took place. (See Maltby, Straker, this volume). Using these techniques it becomes possible to establish the pattern of human exploitation of Exmoor's resources and to explore the relationship between man and his environment which has produced the present landscape. Without the gathering of factual information rather than legend, however appealing, we can neither understand Exmoor's past nor manage its present properly. This understanding not only enables us to enlarge inventories and data banks but also permits interpretation for professional and public dissemination, leading, it is hoped, to greater enjoyment by all and the better attainment of National Park purposes.

The purposes for which National Parks were set up include the preservation of natural beauty and the encouragement of quiet enjoyment by the public. Subsequent guidance added a duty to have care for the social and economic wellbeing of the community and the Edwards Report of 1991, in reviewing the progress of National Parks, recommended the establishment of natural and historic inventories for each Park. It is in the context of these purposes that Exmoor National Park Authority is seeking to investigate and interpret the manmade landscape. The so-called 'natural' beauty consists of an historic landscape with both inanimate and animate components, which form the archaeology and ecology of the countryside.

The archaeology of Exmoor has not received much attention in the past; indeed it seems to have been bypassed or overlooked. The antiquarians of earlier centuries and the archaeologists of the present century were lured to the massive granite monuments of Dartmoor, to Stonehenge and the great earthworks of Wessex and to the palaeoenvironmental wealth of the Somerset Levels. Rather like the Exmoor Pony or the deer, the more subtle historic riches of Exmoor have remained camouflaged in the heather and bracken or hidden deep in the woodlands. Although Exmoor National Park Authority has employed ecological experts for many of its forty years and has built up considerable data on the natural environment, thirty seven years went by before the significance of its historic environment was addressed by the appointment of an archaeologist. There is a lot of catching up to do, not only to achieve a proper understanding of the natural environment for our own purposes, but also to give Exmoor's historic environment its rightful place in both regional and national contexts.

Three years ago the first archaeologist joined the staff of the National Park Authority with the task of tackling these aspirations for Exmoor's historic environment and finding means of achieving them. With so little having been done before, it was not difficult to assess what needed doing; this included almost everything, from basic location and survey to the detailed management and interpretation of individual sites and areas of historic landscape. It was a different matter to find the necessary resources. Starting new areas of work from a low budget level at a time of financial cutbacks is an uphill struggle. It is therefore important to acknowledge the help in cash, kind and personal assistance that has been received in these first three years. We have been fortunate in receiving financial support and expert assistance from the Royal Commission on the Historic Monuments of England in matters of survey and record and from English Heritage for management surveys and scheduling projects. We have also been able to benefit from the expertise of knowledgeable members of the Exmoor community.

The main priority has been to identify the elements and complexities of the historic environment of Exmoor in terms of the location and extent of monuments and sites and the relationships in time and space between them. The primary source of data is usually the County Sites and Monument Register (SMR). In Exmoor's case there are two, Devon and Somerset. Since they are compiled as a result of reported information rather than as a product of programmed information gathering, they do not pretend to be 'complete' records and, in their coverage of Exmoor, they certainly are not. This coverage also emphasises the paucity of fieldwork that has been carried out on Exmoor. An additional hindrance to the use of SMR information and the exchange of data lies in Exmoor's location across the boundary of two counties. Two sources have to be consulted which run on different computer systems, neither of which is immediately compatible with the National Park's own. Perhaps an archaeologist should not mind using traditional paper records but, as this would seem an undesirable devotion to antiquity, we are now tackling information storage and exchange with more appropriate late twentieth century technology.

In addition to the SMRs and the National Monuments Record, which similarly reflects the patchy nature of the record for Exmoor, some archaeological interpretation of aerial photographic cover had been carried out but little had been checked on the ground. Thus in 1991 we had remarkably little to go on and Exmoor had a reputation as something of a black hole in the archaeological landscape. Seeking to remedy this situation we have been extremely fortunate in that the Royal Commission on the Historic Monuments of England (RCHME) were already minded to carry out a survey of Exmoor at some time. A little encouragement, with support at Commissioner level, persuaded them to start sooner rather than later.

As a result, the Exeter Office of the Royal Commission began a six year survey of the National Park in 1992. This survey has begun on the western half of Exmoor and is working towards the east, mapping sites at 1:2,500 scale, with larger-scale plans of particular sites. Two years into its programme, it has already revealed new sites dating from the prehistoric period to the twentieth century and has reinterpreted some existing puzzles and misconceptions. The completion of the survey will provide a major and vital resource for all archaeological work on Exmoor, in that an existing mapped survey is usually a basic tool for any project. In 1991 there were already existing National Park policy objectives and schemes which required the addition of archaeological information. In the main these were, and are, land management projects: the Farm Conservation Scheme, Management Plans for the National Park's own estate, and management plans for particular sites or landscapes. It is inevitable that we carry out these smaller-scale management surveys before the Royal Commission survey is complete. Where the land is outside the previously surveyed area, this involves extra investigation and location during the management survey However, this input is balanced by the resources saved in not having to carry out detailed metric recording, as the RCHME survey can do this systematically within its programme. As with the early stages of the Royal Commission Survey, these management surveys have produced new sites, indicating a far greater density than existing records suggested and shedding new light on past land use. We have benefited from the considerable support given by English Heritage in carrying out archaeological surveys for management.

At this early stage in the evolution of our understanding of the historic environment of Exmoor it is possible only to sketch an outline of the picture which, with time and resources, will become more complete and detailed. Some time from now it is to be hoped that the following summary will be seen as the 'before' snapshot superseded by a more refined and coherent 'after' portrait.

It is apparent from flint scatters at Hawkcombe Head and the foreshore of Porlock Bay that later mesolithic communities exploited both upland and coastal resources. The discovery of flints associated with the submerged forest seaward of the pebble ridge and Porlock Marsh (Boyd Dawkins, 1870) and work in progress by Orford and Jennings, indicating the considerable depth and antiquity of the marsh deposits (Orford and Jennings, unpub. report), hint at the high archaeological and environmental potential of the deposits beneath and behind the ridge. The shingle ridge is threatened by marine incursion (Wilson, this volume), which puts these crucial deposits at risk and we are urgently seeking funds to enable proper assessment of an area which is one of the most important archaeological and palaeoenvironmental sites on Exmoor.

There are no sites on Exmoor scientifically dated to the Neolithic period. The recovery in farming operations of stone axe heads and other artefacts confirms the presence of Neolithic communities, felling trees for timber and for the manufacture of tools, containers and weapons. Wood was a most important material, underrepresented in archaeological records due to its perishability unless waterlogged or mineralised. On Exmoor it is likely to have played a particularly important role as a building material due to the poor quality of native stone. The non-durable nature of the stone in turn helps to explain the apparent scarcity of stone structures and the small scale of lithic monuments here. Evidence for the enclosure of land for agriculture and stock raising is found in the low earth and stone banks of field systems, tracks, clearance cairns and hut circles, visible for example on Codsend Moor, by Chetsford Water and on Holdstone and Trentishoe Downs. These sites have not been scientifically dated, but comparison with similar sites elsewhere suggests a Bronze Age date and hints at the extent to which an articulated manmade landscape, the forerunner of the field patterns we know today, was developing on Exmoor in the later prehistoric period.

Also of Bronze Age date are the burial mounds, or barrows, located singly or in cemetery groups, usually on hill tops, crests and ridges. Notable groups are visible at Chapman Barrows, Five Barrows and Two Barrows (respectively nine barrows and four barrows, in fact) and Wam Barrows. None of these has been excavated to modern standards, though nearly all bear the central hollows which indicate 'opening' in earlier years. These monuments had a primary function as burial places, often with subsequent burials inserted in the mound and probably around it as well. In addition they acted as major landmarks and perhaps as territorial markers, adding further practical and cultural dimensions to the prehistoric landscape of Exmoor. More enigmatic are the lithic monuments of which Exmoor has an abundance. Despite the poor working qualities of local stone, prehistoric communities erected a plethora of geometric settings, rows, circles and single standing stones. Their purpose, apart from the broad category of 'ritual monument', remains unclear. The Longstone, near Challacombe, is exceptional for its height of 3 m; more commonly the stones are knee-high and many hardly break the turf. White Ladder, a double stone row consisting of over 160 stones extending over a quarter of a mile, is a remarkable example of the last, with many of its stones now beneath the surface. This is partly due to expansion of the peaty soil, but the stones could never have stood far above ground level. The monument was located in 1975 by Hazel Eardley-Wilmot and includes many white quartz stones perhaps relying on their glitter, rather than size, for visual impact.

The farming communities of the Iron Age on Exmoor followed the national trend in building large enclosures on apparently defendable hill tops or spurs. Hill-forts, hill-top and hill-slope enclosures of this period can be found as notable landscape features across Exmoor. Apart from their defensive capacity, they would also have provided locations for occupation, trading, exchange and political and recreational meetings. Bat's Castle at Dunster, Cow Castle, in the Barle Valley below Simonsbath, and Shoulsbury are dramatic examples. Less

Plate 19 Cow Castle.

impressive in scale and location, but strategically and functionally important are hill-slope enclosures such as that at Sweetworthy and one, recently discovered, in Timberscombe Wood.

The Roman Conquest seems to have had little demonstrable effect on Exmoor. Apart from the two fortlets at Old Burrow and Martinhoe on the North Devon coast, the existing archaeological evidence suggests that the Romano-British community continued its agricultural existence much as before. However, future discoveries may well change this picture. The two fortlets were built on the cliffs to act as signalling stations, from which small garrisons could keep watch on the coast of South Wales and signal to the Roman fleet in the Bristol Channel in the event of attack. Both sites were excavated in the 1960s, the results showing that Martinhoe superseded Old Burrow and was occupied until c.AD 70, (Fox and Ravenhill 1966).

The early mediaeval period on Exmoor remains, in outdated parlance, something of a Dark Age. The lack of survey and excavation has resulted in little clear evidence for the period but the continuance of an agriculturally-based way of life is suggested by sites such as the recently discovered deserted settlement in Horner Wood. The inscribed stone on Winsford Hill has been dated by epigraphy to the sixth century AD as has the wheel-headed cross inscribed on the terminal of the Culbone stone row. The Royal Forest, with its Forest Law, wardens and grazing procedures, dominated the high moorland through the middle ages until the early nineteenth century, when it was sold by the Crown. Its legacy of control is shown by the remains of telling houses, like the one at Yarde Down, where the livestock were counted as they passed. Wool production was a dominant force in the agricultural economy of mediaeval and postmediaeval Exmoor, the raising of sheep for wool and the ample water supplies to power woollen cloth production created some prosperity. The yarn market in Dunster is a visual reminder of its central importance. The history and archaeology of Exmoor are intimately linked with farming and the farmsteads which have developed, in some cases, over several hundred years. It is likely that proper examination of extant and deserted farmsteads would reveal mediaeval origins in many cases.

As well as the buildings of its settlements and farmsteads, the mediaeval period has left a notable legacy of motte and bailey castles on and around Exmoor. Fine examples at Holwell Castle, Parracombe and Bury Castle, Bury in the Exe Valley have survived unmodified. At Dunster Castle, beside the later magnificence of developments by the Luttrell family, lie the remains of the motte and bailey built by the de Mohuns. Exmoor does not boast many large country houses and Dunster Castle is unusual in its splendour but there have been several large estates established, often as offshoots of primary holdings and seats elsewhere. Though the holdings on Exmoor have frequently been sold on, their owners made their mark on the landscape, both in their architecture and their agricultural regimes. The Acland family at Holnicote, Winsford and Pixton, the last later owned by the Earls of Carnarvon; the Lovelace/Lytton family at Ashley Combe and Lillycombe; the Knights in the former Royal Forest and in the Brendon area; the Chichesters and Fortescues and Hallidays in the western part of the Park and the Chargot Estate and Nettlecombe Court in the east; all left recognisable signatures, from gate-catches to farmhouses, in their farms, cottages and their estate landscapes. No account of the man-made landscape of Exmoor would be

Plate 20 Remains of the Italianate Gardens at Ashley Combe.

complete without inclusion of the industrial revolution which occurred in the second half of the nineteenth century on the Brendon Hills, in the former Royal Forest area and around the periphery of the moor. On the Brendon Hills the peaceful rural community was rudely awakened by the opening of iron mines and the influx of miners who worked them. A light railway built along the hill top from Gupworthy to Brendon Hill brought ore from the mines to the inclined plane which linked it to the standard gauge railway between Comberow and Watchet. This formed the West Somerset Mineral Line, which, with the remains of the mines it served and the miners' settlements, now survive as silent but dramatic and evocative features in the landscape. The enterprise was uneconomic and shortlived, as were the iron mining operations elsewhere, but its traces represent a sample of the wealth of rural industrial remains on Exmoor.

This rapid overview can only hint at the extent and richness of the historic landscape of Exmoor, but it provides a preliminary framework which further survey and research will reshape and consolidate.

It is usual to follow up the general survey of the historic landscape with the examination of particular site or monument types. Such work is in its infancy here but there are three recent or current surveys which illustrate the breadth and depth of the archaeological resource on Exmoor.

THE LITHIC MONUMENTS SURVEY

In 1992, the RCHME completed a survey of the lithic monuments of Exmoor. These enigmatic standing stones, stone rows, settings and circles were the first class of monuments to be comprehensively surveyed and recorded on Exmoor. Subsequently the English Heritage Monument Protection Programme funded a project to schedule nationally important examples.

PILOT SURVEY OF FARMSTEADS

The economic base of Exmoor has been predominantly agricultural for some 6000 years. The archaeology of farming extends from the Neolithic period to the present day and it is essential, in these days of rapid change, that we record and understand the survivals from all periods and preserve the evidence of its development as an integral part of the historic landscape. To this end Maggie Ford has carried out a pilot survey of a sample of farmsteads for the National Park Authority. This has begun to demonstrate not only the development of different types of farms and farming across the Park but also the condition, completeness and extent of conversion of the buildings. This pilot project has enabled us to raise with English Heritage the need for a comprehensive appraisal of farmsteads on Exmoor. We are developing a wider survey, with a view to devising strategies to enable the working farming community to maintain the significant historic farmsteads and buildings of their predecessors.

THE WEST SOMERSET MINERAL LINE

The remains of the remarkable mid-nineteenth century iron extraction enterprises on the Brendon Hills have also received close attention. A report on the condition and potential for consolidation and interpretation of the entire complex of mines, engine houses, railway and inclined plane was carried out in 1993 by Mike Jones. He is now recording and surveying all the extant remains from Gupworthy to Watchet. A joint

Exmoor National Park/West Somerset District Council project group is working towards the preservation of the Line and its associated sites with a view to greater opportunities for public enjoyment.

As a National Park Authority, charged with the preservation of the landscape, the encouragement of public enjoyment and the wellbeing of the local community, it is necessary to seek to balance all these purposes. In terms of the historic environment we are seeking to create a sound record by survey, to encourage and support appropriate management and to enable people to enjoy and understand this rich inheritance. It is by helping those who value their historic environment to care for it and to enjoy it and by offering others opportunities to develop an interest, that the future security of its constituent parts and the whole landscape pattern that they create can best be assured. Exmoor is a working, living landscape and it would be wrong to attempt to fossilise it. Without altering the face of Exmoor's historic landscape to its detriment we can change people's perception of its past and encourage a sense of responsibility for its future. By involving the community in projects such as recording and monitoring sites in their own locality, by keeping them informed about the progress of

Plate 21 *Young archaeologists from Devon learning about Old Burrow from the Ermine Street Guard.*

schemes and by encouraging them to be partners in caring for their inheritance, we can hope to carry them with us in our efforts to care for Exmoor for them and for the whole nation.

REFERENCES

W. Boyd Dawkins, 'On the discovery of flint and chert under a submerged forest in West Somerset', *Journal of the Ethnological Society*, New Series II, (1970) 141-144.

A. Fox and W.L.D. Ravenhill, 'Early Roman Outposts on the North Devon Coast, Old Burrow and Martinhoe', *Proceedings of Devon Archaeological Society*, 24, (1966) 3-39.

SOME ASPECTS OF EXMOOR'S RECENT ECONOMIC HISTORY

Hilary Binding

Education Consultant, Carhampton, Somerset

It goes without saying that Exmoor's economy has centred on agriculture, the cultivation and use of the land for the production of food, from earliest times until the present day. It is only over the last few decades that the tourist industry has replaced farming as the greatest provider of employment and the largest generator of income. This paper outlines the history of human use of Exmoor and investigates some aspects of industry and trade that developed alongside agriculture using the natural resources of the moor and the products of the farms.

The 1700 years from c.400 BC to c.AD 1300 saw much of Exmoor steadily cleared of trees, settled and farmed. Round about 400 BC the climate on Exmoor seems to have changed for the worse and earlier tendencies for people to actually live on the high central plateau of the moor were, on the whole, abandoned though farmers continued to graze stock there during the summer months. Maltby (this volume) suggests that maybe Bronze Age man faced an early environmental disaster linked with the over-exploitation of the high moor. During the Iron Age people built settlements of a defensive nature like Bat's Castle (Carhampton) and Shoulsbury Camp (Challacombe) at relatively high altitudes, as well as farms on hillslopes where there was more shelter, as at Bury Castle (Selworthy) and Sweetworthy (Luccombe). Recent investigations in, for example, Horner Woods and at Carhampton, confirm that Iron Age settlement was relatively widespread with people living and working in the lower valleys and near the coast.

Roman influence on Exmoor was negligible and it seems probable that while Iron Age farmers may have used Roman coins and pottery they generally continued a traditional way of life centred around their settlements and farmsteads. About AD 600 there seems to have been something of a Saxon aristocratic take-over of Exmoor and soon after 700 Saxon families were moving into the area, looking for places to settle and presumably developing some sort of rapport – or the opposite – with those already living there. There was plenty of room. Anyone standing on the top of Dunkery Hill at the time would have looked down onto a heavily wooded landscape broken by tiny clearings each marked by a spiral of smoke. The Saxons chose good sites for their farmsteads but as they cleared the woodland they may, at first, have avoided the Celtic settlements rather as people do who are looking for a space to occupy on a beach.

As the population grew, it became necessary to clear more land for new homes and more small fields. Most Saxons settled on lower ground on or below the spring lines but there were at least one or two hardy pioneers such as Raeda, farming at Radworthy, 366 m up at the head of a small combe below Chapman Barrows while at Lank Combe (long combe) which runs west from Badgworthy Water below Brendon Common, Edwin was farming on his own in 1086 (Hoskins, *Devon*, 55). Perhaps the people who chose such isolated spots when there was still plenty of lower land available were occupying sites originally settled in the Iron Age. Because many of these Saxon settlements have now become villages there is a tendency to assume that the Saxons settled in villages but this is not so. Rather, they settled in farmsteads and hamlets. Some of the latter were later to develop into the villages but the pattern at the time was of small isolated holdings.

The idea of continuous occupation and land use, of people taking over earlier farm sites, is an absorbing one which has been studied particularly by Mick Aston. One good example of successive occupation can be found at Sweetworthy, Bagley (SS 8824260) and Hagley (SS 823425) on the borders of Luccombe and Stoke Pero parishes where two ringworks of unproven but probable prehistoric date have been superseded by two farmsteads: one Sweetworthy, probably abandoned in the Middle Ages; the other, Bagley in use until the late nineteenth century (Aston,Landscape, 70). On North Hill the remains of the Domesday vill of Myne, held before the conquest by the Saxon Leofwin, lie within a quarter of a mile of Furzebury Brake, an Iron Age settlement with excellent views across the channel, while on the coast, just outside the Park boundary, recent exploratory excavations at Carhampton indicate the existence of an earlier Saxon settlement with a possible Iron Age settlement close by. The evidence for continuity of land use, if not of actual farmsteads, is strong and hints at widespread, if scattered, occupation of all but the central area of moorland at a relatively early date. There is a great deal more work to be done.

During the Saxon and later medieval period the general pattern of farming on Exmoor was of the homestead surrounded by small 'in-bye' fields permanently under cultivation and surrounded, in their turn, by a larger expanse of 'out-field' parts of which were broken up and cultivated for a few years and then returned to 'waste'. This land and other 'commons' were used for summer grazing, chiefly of sheep, but also of cattle and horses. The open field system of farming in strips, with three days work for the lord and three for the tenant, was found more generally in the west of England than used to be thought but not usually on higher ground. The open communal field seems to have been adopted near the larger settlements while Minehead clearly had three fields; remnants of the Northfield

and the strip pattern can be seen on the tithe map of 1843 and on some of the early photographs of North Hill.

THE MEDIEVAL WOOLLEN INDUSTRY

The number of Exmoor farms continued to expand until the fourteenth century when Exmoor farming reached an early zenith, perhaps coincidental with the development of the woollen industry. After that the number of farmsteads began to decline although the area of land under cultivation probably stayed much the same as the remaining farms expanded. It was the demand for wool that brought the Exmoor farmer into the business world.

At first, sheep's wool from the family flock was used to clothe the backs of lord and peasant alike; the processes of washing, carding and combing, spinning the yarn and weaving and finishing the cloth, all being carried out at home. As early as the 1100s some surplus wool may have been taken to nearby towns like Tiverton and South Molton for processing but the real breakthrough in the industry came for Exmoor with the introduction of the fulling mill to this country in 1185. These water-powered fulling stocks replaced the old, slow method of fulling cloth with the feet, similar to treading grapes. Until the advent of the mill, towns were the centres of commercial woollen operations but the fulling mills needed supplies of fast-running water to drive the wheels that powered them and so were sited out in the countryside. One of the first fulling mills in the area was at Taunton but soon there were mills at Dunster (1259), North Molton (1314) and Dulverton (1340). Fields called 'The Racks' where the fulled cloth was stretched out to dry on racks or tenterbeds can be found close to many villages. Inevitably, weavers and dyers followed the fulling mills and new centres of the industry were established and were to flourish until the turn of the nineteenth century.

By 1266 Adam the Dyer, Walter the Webber (weaver), Alice the Webber, Christina the Webber and William the Fuller were all working in Dunster while fifty years later in Brompton Regis, Adam le Webbe, Simone le Touker and Michaelo le Spiner are named in the 1327 lay subsidy list. By the 1600s there are four Webbers in Brompton Regis and Webbers, Toukers (fullers),

Dyers and Comers in many of the villages indicating a widespread degree of specialism.

It was common for the farmer's family to be involved in carding the wool and in spinning it. John Hooker writing in his *Synopsis Chorographical of Devon* in 1599 says:

> There is no market nor village nor scarse any private mannes house where in theise clothes be not made, or that there is not spinninge or cordinge for the same: as the dalye travellers can so witnes it for wheresoever any man doth travell you will fynde at the hall dore as they do name the foredore of the house he shall I say fynde the wiffe theire children and theire servantes at the turn spynninge or at theire cardes cardinge and by wyh commoditie the common people do lyve.

In 1791, Collinson, in *The History and Antiquities of the County of Somerset* commended the spinners of Porlock and of Carhampton for the quality of their yarn. A drawing in the Braikenridge Collection (SANHS) made c.1845 shows the interior of a cottage in the Doone Valley with a large spinning wheel or 'turne' taking a prominent position in the kitchen. The yarn was sent down to the busy market centres for weaving and finishing.

By the sixteenth century the wealth of many Exmoor farmers was based in wool. The will of Thomas Almysworthy of Exford, proved on 3 May 1530, includes bequests of sheep to maintain lights in the parish church, a sheep to his godson, William Crocombe and also to his goddaughter at Norrys, a 'yew and a lambe' to his daughter and child and 'ii yewys and lammys' to William Daw his servant. The rest of the flock was left to his wife and his sons. Sheep left to maintain lights and for godchildren were common bequests in Exford in the years that followed and also in other parishes like, for example, Brompton Ralph, Brompton Regis, Cutcombe, Dulverton and Upton (Wells Wills, Weaver). In Dunster in 1443 there was enough wealth for the people of the town to contract with Jon Marys of Stoke Courcy (Stogursey) to build a fine new church tower. The clothiers, or middlemen, who bought in the yarn, put it out to weavers and finishers and were responsible for the sale of the finished cloth probably reaped the richest rewards.

Plate 22 *Pack horse bridge at Lyncombe, near Exford.*

The wool, yarn and finished cloth was carried to market centres like Tiverton and Barnstaple on the backs of pack ponies in panniers or hung from crooks or hooks. Strings of nine or so ponies must have been a common sight making their way sure-footedly on stony tracks like Yellowcombe Lane at Winsford and crossing rivers on the narrow packhorse bridges that can still be found in the most remote spots. There were said to be eighty pack ponies in Molland at the end of the eighteenth century.

MARKETS AND PORTS

By the 1200s a few Exmoor manors had been created boroughs by their lords in the hope that speculation might lead to personal profit and an increased income from tolls and rents. In Combe Martin, Dunster and South Molton, tenements were held by free burgage in return for a money rent, and a weekly market and annual fair held. This regular commerce brought a new impetus to the countryside round about, encouraging farmers to produce a surplus for sale and providing opportunities to purchase goods from elsewhere as well as opening up a window onto the outside world. People moved to find work in these developing towns, though it must be said that only South Molton and Dunster fulfilled their potential as boroughs. Perhaps the relatively isolated situation of places like North Molton, which was certainly known as a borough, meant that there were not enough visiting traders to make a success of things. Porlock and Dulverton were also granted weekly markets. Porlock became a busy little centre for the surrounding area but at Dulverton, the market seems at first to have brought little prosperity to the town which in the 1540s was described as being 'in decay'. A new charter was to follow.

While the ports along Exmoor's coastline remained relatively insignificant compared with the great maritime centres on the south coast of Devon, they nonetheless played an essential part in the economy of Exmoor. Grahame Farr in *Ships and Harbours of Exmoor* points out that the history of each port differs considerably. Ilfracombe was the largest port but because of its position and sheltered harbour developed into more of a refuge and service port than a trading centre while in the sixteenth and seventeenth centuries Minehead became the staple port for the wool trade. In the eighteenth century the larger ports including Porlock Weir and Lynmouth began to increase their coastal fleets; ketches, sloops, brigs and schooners. Some plied between other ports carrying, for example, Welsh coal to Cornwall and Cornish copper and tin for smelting in South Wales. Others moved regularly between their home ports, South Wales, Bristol and Ireland carrying market produce, household effects and also passengers, who were, for example, able to save a long journey through Bristol by joining direct the Milford packet for Ireland.

A wide variety of goods was carried including sheep, cattle, salt, wine, wood, raisins, oysters, butter and salmon. There were cargoes of spices from the West Indies and at least one cargo of 'elifand's teeth'. Iron ore was imported for use by the village blacksmiths who fashioned implements and tools and items for the home. Their fuel was the charcoal produced from pre-historic times in most of Exmoor's ancient, broad-leaved woodlands including those at Culbone, Nutcombe Bottom at Dunster, the Barle Woods above Dulverton and Watersmeet. Recently ancient charcoal burning sites have been discovered in Horner Woods.

Raw wool, yarn and finished cloth were taken in and out of Minehead while hides were imported for tanning and oak bark exported for use in the industry elsewhere. There were tanneries in many villages and some survived as commercial businesses until this century. Besides the men employed in the tanneries the industry involved those who worked on allotments in the woodlands, coppicing the oak trees and stripping the tanbark from young growth to provide the tannin for curing hides. Later in the nineteenth century pit props were a common cargo destined for the South Wales' coal mines.

Even the smallest inlets like Heddon's Mouth and Wooda Bay had a certain amount of trade. Boats brought in culm and limestone for burning at the beach-head kilns which, depending on the state of the tide, might be off-loaded at the harbour or, alternatively, the cargo thrown overboard onto the beach to be collected by horse and cart (Corner, *Porlock*, 20). Most small ports imported coal for household use as well as groceries. Watermouth was the service port for the nearby village of Berrynarbor and occasionally, during the summer months in the later 1800s, small sailing boats known as the 'Strawberry Boats' carried luscious, locally-grown strawberries to Swansea.

Plate 23 The Perriton *(right) in Minehead harbour c.1890.*

Evidence of ship-building can be found for many of the local ports. In the eighteenth century some 64 vessels, mostly sloops of 40-50 tons, were built at Ilfracombe and at Minehead there was a ship-building yard to the west of the harbour where about a dozen brigs and sloops were built between 1752 and 1816 (Farr). The last vessel to be built at Minehead was the schooner, *Perriton*, built in 1881 at the head of the beach near Blenheim Road, by Benjamin Williams of Watchet.

For centuries fishing was an important aspect of the economy of the ports. In the Dunster Castle accounts for the early 1400s fish often features. On one occasion salmon, milwell, lyng and hake were bought in Minehead and wrapped in canvas to be sent to Southampton en route for Harfleur where Sir Hugh Luttrell was in residence as Seneschal of Normandy. From the 1700s herring were caught in quantity by boats from all the larger Exmoor ports and sold on the quay or delivered around the villages. In the last few decades the herring have left the area and there is now little commercial fishing. The harbours are instead filled with yachts and other small pleasure craft.

THE FOREST

I do not intend to go into detail concerning the Royal Forest that lay at the heart of the moor for its story, as well as the story of its later reclamation, has been thoroughly researched and is told in many other places. This area of the moor, not wooded but an area 'foras' or outside ordinary law and where game was reserved for royal use was first described as a forest in 1204. It would be wrong to suppose that the king often made a point of coming to hunt in the area though it is said that there was a royal hunting lodge at Brompton Regis. Instead huntsmen were sent to catch the red deer for the royal table as in 1259 when 'Robert de Candevr' and 'William de Candevr' were sent 'to take 30 harts for the kings use in the forest of Exmor' (Calendar of Close Rolls, 1259). Local lords were also granted the right to hunt in the forest thus augmenting the supply of game for their own tables but far more important to the medieval and later economy of the region was the regulated letting of the forest for summer grazing by sheep, cattle and horses which continued over a period of more than 600 years and benefited many local farmers.

In the past there has been a tendency to look to the enclosure of the forest at the beginning of the nineteenth century as providing the initiative for agricultural change and improvement on Exmoor. It certainly was influential but well before this date changes were already taking place. For example, the Quartlys, tenants at Higher Champson and West Molland from 1703 to 1890, were breeding Red Devon cattle considered by the agriculturalist, Billingsley, to be the best draught oxen in the land. At Dunster, in the mid 1700s, Henry Fownes Luttrell and his agent had initiated a long term plan for improving the Dunster estates; on the one hand, landscaping the castle, providing better access, adding a folly on Conygar Hill and creating a new Deer Park and, on the other, beginning to rationalise the farms on the estates. Amongst the Luttrell papers, held at the Somerset Record Office, are surveys, maps and working notes (DD/L 1/40/26) which show how, by degrees, the small-holdings based in the village of Carhampton, were taken in hand and much of the land redistributed to form three new farms; Townsend (or Western) Farm, The Pantyl'd (or Eastern) Farm, and Troytes which was to amalgamate with Escotts and Millets and, much later, become known as Winsors Farm. The earlier small-holdings varied in size between about 8 and 42 acres and in most cases included a five bedroomed house and land spread across the parish incorporating arable, pasture, wet meadow, common grazing land, woodland and, on the beach, weares and 'stackes' for fishing. By 1790 the three new farms had been let, the old houses rebuilt and the process of independent small holders becoming dependent labourers begun. In the higher part of the parish at Rodhuish on the slopes of the Brendon Hills there was a different pattern for by the early eighteenth century the small farms had already been broken up and the land amalgamated to form substantial holdings.

LIME

The enclosure of Exmoor Forest and reclamation of the land for cropping demanded a large supply of lime to sweeten the soil and it became necessary to expand the import not only of culm with which to burn the limestone but the limestone itself. The lime kilns along the beaches mark where the imported limestone was burnt. At one time there were eighteen kilns in

Combe Martin and much of this lime was conveyed by horse and cart to the Knight estates. A watercolour by J.M.W Turner dated about 1824, depicts one of these kilns and shows not only the kiln but also some highly practical woman who is hanging out her washing nearby where the heat from the furnace will help it dry. There were kilns at Woody Bay, Lynmouth and Porlock Weir as well as at Bossington and Minehead where in 1622 the duty on imported limestone was $^1/_2$d per ton.

Pockets of limestone can be found across Exmoor in the Ilfracombe Beds that run from Combe Martin across the centre of the moor surfacing at Simonsbath and on the Brendon Hills. Every outcrop was exploited and limestone was quarried all up the valley at Combe Martin and at many other places including Allercott near Timbersombe, Cutcombe and Newlands near Exford. There were also limestone quarries at Alcombe.

At Newland Quarry (SS 824385) as at most of these sites, limestone was both quarried and burnt. The Newlands site comprised two large quarries, both now flooded. The smaller one to the west served three small kilns and was disused by 1887. The larger, with its complex of kilns, inclines, lime store, cart shed and smithy, was worked until 1914. Farmers from the Exford area would travel down to Porlock to fetch culm by horse and cart coming back by the old Limeway. I was told by Dick Marley, late of Chibbet Ford, who used to work at Newland Quarry, that while the lime was being burnt the farmers would stable their horses and sit down to play cards until it was ready to be loaded to take back to the farm. Mr Marley showed me the site of a railway along which trucks with culm and limestone were carried to be loaded directly into the top of the kilns. Lime kilns near Raleigh's Cross were built when the limestone and fuel could be brought to the site by rail.

BUILDING MATERIALS

Although many houses on Exmoor were built originally of wood, cob and thatch many of those that have survived were enlarged or rebuilt using local sandstone. Nearly every farm, hamlet and village has, close by, a quarry from which stone has been used over generations for local building. Near the coast beach pebbles were often used as well. Since the sandstone was not resilient to weathering it was customary to coat the walls with regular applications of lime-wash. Slate is common on the moor both for roofing and for facing houses particularly exposed to the elements. The blue slate quarry at Treborough, owned by the Trevelyan family at Nettlecombe, was worked intermittently from the 1400s until its final closure in 1938. It provided slate for roofing as well as slate slabs for many purposes from doorsteps and flagstones to porch overhangs and tombstones. From the 1700s bricks and tiles were made at the Luttrell's brickyard at Dunster and stone was occasionally imported by sea for special jobs like the restoration of Dunster Castle and the building of the Gatehouse in the 1420s when freestone was brought from Bristol and tile-stones from Cornwall.

MINING

Exmoor's small scattered seams of mineral ores have been mined sporadically for centuries and at different times, usually for short periods, have provided increased employment and brought new money to the area. It was not, however, until the nineteenth century that landowners, encouraged by the success of industrialists in other parts of the country, tried to exploit the extraction of minerals more thoroughly.

At Combe Martin the productive silver lead mines were worked on and off from the end of the thirteenth century until 1875 when they were finally abandoned. The Bampfylde and Poltimore mines in the Heasley Mill area were worked at intervals during the seventeenth and eighteenth centuries but their most profitable period was between 1870 and 1890 when various ores, chiefly copper with some iron, silver and a little gold, were extracted. The nearby Florence Mine at Tabor Hill yielded large quantities of spathic iron ore suitable for steel-making by the Bessemer process. The ores were transported by a narrow gauge tramway to a junction with the Devon and Somerset Railway near South Molton. When John Knight took over his new estates in 1819 he hoped to exploit the ore on his land and had a railway line with incline to Porlock Weir planned and laid out. Under his son, Frederic, ventures at Wheal Eliza and at Cornham were begun enthusiastically but were not to prove economically viable in spite of investment from the Dowlais Iron Company and were eventually abandoned. The full story of mining on the Knight, and later, Fortescue, property can be read in Roger Burton's *The Heritage of Exmoor*.

On the Brendon Hills rich seams of iron ore were mined extensively and fairly profitably from 1853 to 1878, the West Somerset Mineral Line being constructed to transport the ore to Watchet for shipping to South Wales. Three hundred or so miners from Cornwall and Wales moved into the area and almost overnight, the villages of Brendon Hill and Gupworthy sprang up, complete with differentiated housing, church and chapels, school, stores and a teetotal guest house. The mines were worked successfully for a few years but the high cost of transporting the ore to South Wales for smelting and later competition from the import of high quality ore from Spain soon made the venture uneconomic and the mines finally closed in 1883. Later attempts to revive the industry proved short-lived.

In spite of these initiatives, the enclosure of the moor and improvements on lowland farms the economy of Exmoor was generally depressed. The woollen industry had declined rapidly due to competition from the mechanisation of the industry in the north of England. At Dulverton and Heasley Mill manufactories were built for the production of serge but they survived only until the 1830s although the Dulverton factory turned to the production of silk crepe until the 1860s. Villages like Porlock and Dunster were in a poor state. Some were still little more than hamlets and needed the leadership of a reforming parson like Joseph Relph at Exford or the investment of land-owners like the Aclands at Holnicote, the Knights and the Hallidays at Glenthorne to bring improved living conditions, more job opportunities and eventually some degree of prosperity. While prospects remained poor labourers left the land to look for employment in the towns of South Wales and, in some cases, Australia and Canada.

THE TOURIST INDUSTRY

But change was on its way. Towards the end of the eighteenth century, as the French Wars prevented the wealthy from taking the Grand Tour of Europe and the search for the Picturesque became fashionable, people began to appreciate the delights of Exmoor's scenery and a veritable 'tourist trail' developed. Mr Doveton, following the route in 1797, kept a notebook of exquisite watercolor and pen and ink sketches showing beach huts at Minehead and picturesque views of North Hill, Porlock, Culbone and the Valley of Rocks, Brendon and Dulverton. This is exactly the route that our apparent poetic pioneers, Samuel Taylor Coleridge, William Wordsworth and later Robert Southey, took when they visited Exmoor and became, in effect, the moor's first publicity association. Many were to follow, crossing the moor and enjoying the 'romantick' scenery like members of the Esdaile family from Taunton who in 1810 indulged themselves with ' the pleasing expectation of exploring these beautiful and romantic scenes which the Northern coast of Somerset and Devon offers to the traveller'.

The fashionable belief in the efficacy of sea-bathing which had led to the development of places like Brighton and Weymouth in the eighteenth century, contributed to the growth of attractively sited seaside towns as resorts. Both Minehead and Ilfracombe were able to offer sea-bathing as well as access to the moors and soon Lynton and Lynmouth, too, were changing from grubby

Plate 24 Kennisham Engine House, Brendon Hills (now demolished).

fishing villages into thriving resorts. We should perhaps be grateful to the Atlantic weather and a certain inaccessibility for the fact that the whole Exmoor coast was not converted into resorts in the Torquay style for many investors were on the look out for places to develop. When Elizabeth Ernst and her husband visited the area in 1845 she wrote of Porlock Weir:

> It occurred to us that if the three principal landowners, Lord Lovelace, Sir T. Acland and Captain Blathwayt, put their heads & purses together & became a joint stock society, or would afford the necessary facilities for creating one by adequate grants of land on building leases, Porlock might become a very pretty romantic bathing place with detached villas commanding the sea and a fine Crescent almost on the Beach adapting itself to the form of the Bay.

In 1885, the speculator, Colonel Benjamin Lake, bought the Martinhoe estates and set out to turn Wooda Bay into a second Lynmouth building hotels, houses to let, a swimming pool and a pier so that steamers might call and disgorge visitors to enjoy the scenery and spend money in the area perhaps at the inn he proposed to build. Lake also intended to install a cliff railway and a branch line link with the Lynton and Barnstaple Railway but these dreams were not to materialise. The pier was destroyed by storms and Lake turned out to be a rogue. In 1900 he went bankrupt but when the estates were put on the market they were still described fulsomely as 'ripe for further development ... as a popular Pleasure Resort...'

The coming of the railways was another great influence on the development of Exmoor as a tourist area. At Minehead local gentry and business men combined to bring a rail link to the town in 1874 and to build new hotels and lodging houses for the expected rush of visitors. They were not disappointed and by the 1880s Minehead had become a popular resort. Visitors continued to enjoy segregated bathing and outings by carriage or coach and four to Horner Woods, Porlock Weir, Lynton, including the Valley of Rocks and Watersmeet, Dunster and Cleeve Abbey. They took walks on North Hill and some succeeded in getting lost in Selworthy Woods in spite of Sir Thomas Dyke Acland's carefully laid out paths.

Exmoor is traditionally sporting country but the late nineteenth century saw what had been the preserve of the local squire and parson develop into another aspect of tourism. The revival of the Devon and Somerset Staghounds in 1855 under the Mastership of Mr Mordaunt Fenwick Bisset, M.P., of Pixton Park, and the building of the kennels at Exford some twenty years later, together with the advent of the railway to the south of the moor meant an influx of a different type of visitor. People now thronged to Dulverton, Exford and Porlock for sporting holidays. The hunting season was followed by shooting and fishing and initiatives were developed to take full advantage of the demand. The impact on the economy was immediate as people seized the opportunity to provide stabling, accommodation and transport as well as related services like tailoring for the London market.

Properties were let as hunting boxes and former inns like the Castle at Porlock, the Fox and Goose at Parracombe and the White Horse at Exford were improved to accommodate visitors. The Carnarvon Arms at Brushford, built right beside Dulverton railway station offered 'hunters and horses' and 'five miles of fishing on the Barle and the Exe' not to mention a horse bus link between station and town. Hunter's Inn at Parracombe which, at the beginning of the century, had been

Plate 25 The bridge at Exford. On the left is the unimproved White Horse with The Crown in the background.

Plate 26 Old Dulverton station.

simply a farm where local men met in the kitchen to talk over mugs of ale, was taken over in 1868 by the Berry family who began to encourage visitors from the nearby towns and were soon calling it an inn. The premises were burnt down in 1895 and rebuilt soon after in the ubiquitous 'Victorian' style.

While farming continued as the mainstay of the moor's economy more and more people were finding employment providing for visitors and many a farmer's wife was glad to welcome passing walkers into the house for a glass of milk or some bread and cheese. Before long, changing transport and more leisure time brought people into the villages. In the thirties they often stayed for a week or two using the bus service to visit places of interest. Now people are more likely to spend just a few nights in bed and breakfast accommodation and use their cars to get about.

The designation of Exmoor as a National Park has helped to keep recreation within bounds balancing the needs of the visitor with those of conservation and of the people who live and work on the moor, many of whom are turning from being food providers to being tourist providers and park managers. Exmoor's prosperity may no longer depend on the production of food but does still depend on the moor itself.

SELECT BIBLIOGRAPHY

M. Aston, 'Deserted Farmsteads on Exmoor and the Lay Subsidy of 1327 in West Somerset', *PSANS*, (1983).

M. Aston, 'Land Use and Field Systems', in M. Aston, ed., *'Aspects of the Medieval Landscape of Somerset'*, (Taunton, 1988).

H. Binding, *Exmoor – 40 Years On*, (Tiverton, 1994).

H. Binding and V. Bonham-Carter, *Old Dulverton and Around*, (Dulverton, 1986).

H. Bridle, *Woody Bay*, (Woody Bay, 1991).

R.A.Burton, *The Heritage of Exmoor*, (Barnstaple, 1989).

D Corner, *Porlock in Those Days*, (Tiverton, 1992).

G. Court, *Exmoor National Park*, (Exeter, 1987).

G.Farr, *Ships and Harbours of Exmoor*, (Dulverton, 1970).

G.Farr, *Somerset Harbours*, (1954).

L.V. Grinsell, *The Archaeology of Exmoor*, (Newton Abbot, 1970).

W.G.Hoskins, *Devon*, 2nd edition, (Tiverton, 1987).

H.C. Maxwell-Lyte, *The History of Dunster*, (2.vols.), (1909).

D.W.Warren, 'Newland Quarry', *Somerset Industrial Archaeological Society Journal*, Vol.2, (1977) 36-39.

D.W.Warren, 'The Woollen Trade around Exmoor', *SIAS Bulletin*, No. 63, (August 1993) 9-15.

WOODLAND IN THE EXMOOR NATIONAL PARK

Stephen Essex

Department of Geographical Sciences, University of Plymouth

INTRODUCTION

Woodlands are an integral component of the Exmoor scene. The variety of woodland types on Exmoor, such as the coastal woods in the north, the semi-natural woods in the valleys of the south, the coniferous plantations in the east and the woods and beech hedgerows scattered throughout the area, contribute greatly to the landscape character and wildlife value of the National Park. The boundary of the National Park was itself partly influenced by the presence of woodland. The Hobhouse Report of 1947, in considering the designation of Exmoor as a National Park, fixed its southern and eastern boundary to include 'the beautifully wooded valleys of the Exe, Barle and Haddeo' (Hobhouse, 1947). Moreover, Exmoor possesses the unique attribute in its high upland zones – an area known through documentary records to have been largely devoid of trees since the eleventh century and probably earlier – of deliberately planted nineteenth century beech hedges which add an extraordinary and rich dimension to the high moorland scene (Plate 27). Without woodlands, Exmoor's scenery would be considerably diminished not only in aesthetic terms but also in the range of natural habitats which the park supports and the mix of resources which can be derived.

The work of the National Park Authority (NPA) for Exmoor [the Exmoor National Park Committee (ENPC, 1954-1974) and the Exmoor National Park Authority (ENPA, 1974-date)] has

Plate 27 *General view of Exmoor's upland zone showing moorland in far background and beech hedges landscape in foreground. View from the Punchbowl on Winsford Hill looking northwards to Staddon Hill.*

therefore included woodland conservation and management as a vital part of its activities, particularly with respect to the control of coniferous afforestation on the one hand and the encouragement of broadleaved woodland management on the other. The profile of the woodland management issue on Exmoor has, however, been largely overshadowed by the emphasis given to the issue of moorland conservation. The loss of moorland through agricultural improvement is immediate and obvious, whereas a serious deterioration in woodland condition and extent only becomes apparent after several decades of neglect. Nevertheless, the NPA for Exmoor has responded to the challenges of woodland conservation and management through policy initiatives that are appropriate and often innovative. In many respects, the development of the National Park's woodland policy on Exmoor can be seen to be at the forefront of woodland intervention, setting the standard and example for other National Parks. In particular, the ENPA, which now owns more woodland than any other National Park, has provided opportunities to develop and practise exemplary woodland management practises and approaches.

This chapter reviews the historical development of the woodland resource on Exmoor; the present extent, composition and distribution of woodlands on Exmoor; and the evolution of woodland intervention by the NPA for Exmoor over the period 1954-1994. The development of the NPA's woodland policy is traced by means of original archive work using the NPA's committee minutes and other publications. This material provides detailed insights into the circumstances and constraints which have influenced the formulation, implementation and effectiveness of National Park intervention in this aspect of land use change on Exmoor over the first forty years of the National Park's existence.

HISTORICAL BACKGROUND

The evolution of woodland on Exmoor began at the end of the last glaciation (c.20,000 BP) (Figure 14). The glacier advance stopped on a line between the Rivers Severn and Thames, just to the north of what is now Exmoor. Cold climatic conditions which then prevailed created an arctic tundra vegetation type of dwarf willow and birch (Curtis, 1984). As the glaciers retreated, growing conditions began to improve and the tundra vegetation was slowly replaced. Sea levels were lower than today as the water was frozen into ice sheets. Consequently, the British Isles were connected to the continent allowing the influx of a succession of vegetation from the warmer and forested areas of the south. By about 8000 BP, larger birches, Scots pine and hazel had begun to dominate the highland area,

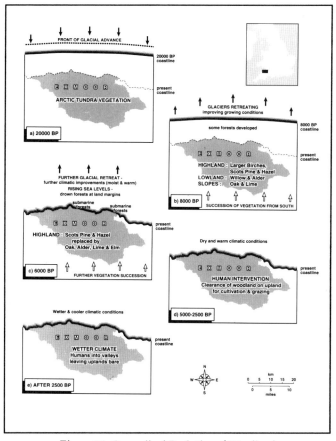

Figure 14 Generalised Evolution of Woodland Cover on Exmoor (20,000BP - 2500BP).

willow and alder the lower land and oak and lime on slopes and in the combes. With further improvement in climate to moist and warm conditions, from about 6000 BP, broadleaved trees, such as oak, alder, lime and elm began to flourish alongside the pine and hazel and perhaps replaced them in the more favoured areas (Court, 1987). Rising sea levels at this time drowned forests which had formed at the land margins. Remnants of submerged forests still exist in Porlock Bay and off Minehead beach (Curtis, 1984).

An increasingly important factor in the reduction of birch and pine, and indeed the woodland resource in general, was active clearance of forest by human intervention. The onset of dry and warm summer conditions between 5000 BP and 2500 BP made Exmoor a suitable place to settle. The clearance is thought to have started in the uplands because the tree cover was thinner, and so easier to remove with simple tools, and because the cleared land was the most suitable for primitive agriculture and pasture. The grazing of livestock prevented the regeneration of young trees and the increasing human population continued the clearance of trees.

Another change in climate after c. 2500 BP to wetter and cooler summer conditions forced the permanent population into the valleys for shelter from the inclement upland areas. This climatic change, together with the human interference, ensured that natural tree growth on the uplands would not return. The major development in the distribution of trees on Exmoor occurred in the eighth century when the Saxon population utilised the lower-lying, most fertile and sheltered lands for a pattern of agriculture dotted with farms, hamlets and small fields, creating the broad pattern of the present day landscape. The first relatively systematic written record of woodlands on Exmoor was the Domesday Book of 1086 and interpretation of its information by Darby and Welldon-Finn (1967) indicates a distribution that was very similar to today's pattern of cover. Figure 15 shows that there was more woodland in the form of tall trees (silva) than underwood consisting of areas of coppice or scrub (silva minuta). The Exmoor uplands appear devoid of tree cover.

It was also in the Saxon period that Exmoor was increasingly valued for its hunting and became a Royal Forest. Forest, in this sense of the word, did not necessarily imply the presence of trees but a tract of land where deer and certain other animals were reserved for the king and protected by Forest Law. The protection and administration afforded by the Crown virtually excluded agricultural activities for several centuries (Curtis, 1984). Exmoor Forest covered about 32,376 ha (80,000 acres) at its greatest extent. After 1301, when Edward I disafforested the eastern part, Forest Law decayed. By about 1400, the boundaries coincided with what is now the parish of Exmoor,

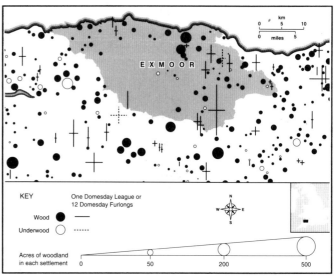

Figure 15 Domesday woodland on Exmoor in 1086.
Source: Darby and Welldon-Finn (1967, p176).

covering an area of about 8094 ha (20,000 acres) in the heart of the modern National Park (Miles, 1972).

The dominant form of woodland management from the Middle Ages until the mid-nineteenth century was coppicing. This produces a self-sustaining crop as shoots regenerate from the cut stump. Woodlands were utilised for a range of purposes and products by the rural populations of Exmoor, such as for pannage (feeding of livestock on acorns or beech mast), building materials, charcoal for smelting and tan bark for curing skins. These uses provided the incentive for woodland management in the past, and their decline in modern times and the related reduction in demand for supplies of wood helps to explain the present day management neglect of broadleaved woodlands.

A notable fashion in the eighteenth century was the tree-planting and landscaping undertaken by the owners of landed estates. The stimulus to treeplanting may indeed be traced to John Evelyn's plea made in 1664 for more timber to meet shortages facing the navy and other users. This demand was combined with favourable economic returns and with the growing fashion for aesthetic improvements eventually culminating in the work of landscape gardeners, such as 'Capability' Brown and Humphry Repton. Examples on Exmoor include Dunster Deer Park (by Henry Fownes Luttrell), Nettlecombe Deer Park, Pixton Park near Dulverton (by Dr John Kent) and Holnicote Estate at Selworthy (by Sir Thomas Acland). These parkland landscapes add another important dimension to the woodland scene on Exmoor.

The timber shortages experienced during the early nineteenth century exacerbated by the demands of the Napoleonic Wars forced parliament to consider the use of Crown lands and forests for timber production. A new Government department, the Commissioners of HM Woods, Forests and Land Revenues, was established in 1810 and commissioned a survey of Exmoor in 1812. The report of this survey, produced in 1814 by Richard Hawkins, recommended that large parts of Exmoor Forest could be planted with oak, ash, beech, birch, larch and fir and suggested that 'allotments' of the moor should be sold, keeping the King's Allotment for forestry. By 1818 the Commissioners had realised that it was impracticable to grow oak forests on Exmoor and sold off the King's Allotment by tender to John Knight, an industrialist from Worcestershire. After this sale, the Royal Forest ceased to exist in law.

John Knight considered Exmoor to be a place for improvement and set about enhancing the land on the estate. He undertook deep ploughing to improve the land, although results were limited by climatic conditions. He also undertook planting, particularly in the Simonsbath area, with beeches along the hedgebanks enclosing new fields (Orwin and Sellick, 1970). These improvements remain an important and distinctive feature of the Exmoor landscape (Plate 28).

In the twentieth century, the creation of the Forestry Commission (FC), with its objective of building up a strategic reserve of timber through its own planting and the encouragement of private landowners has led to afforestation in the form of large coniferous tracts. The main part of the FC's own planting is concentrated in the east of the National Park, particularly on Croydon and Kennisham Hills. Although these

Plate 28 Beech tree hedgebanks on South Hill planted to improve the agricultural value of the moorland in the nineteenth century.

plantations are coniferous and were planted to strictly economic criteria, their effect on the landscape is not totally detrimental as in some other parts of the country. This planting adds another dimension to the woodland and forest landscape of Exmoor.

WOODLAND RESOURCE ON EXMOOR

The present extent, composition and distribution of woodland on Exmoor is the product of these historical influences. Estimates of the total area of woodland on Exmoor vary considerably. According to the most recent figures, prepared for the Section 3 Conservation map in 1990, the present extent of woodland cover in the Exmoor National Park is 8400 ha or about 12 % of the National Park area (ENPA, 1991). This figure includes the principal woodlands together with all small woodlands, shelterbelts and copses identified from air photographs. However, an earlier figure calculated by the Centre for Agricultural Strategy at the University of Reading (1980) put the woodland area on Exmoor at 6957 ha or 10.1% of the National Park area (CAS, 1980). The Exmoor Woodland Survey by the Somerset Trust for Nature Conservation (STNC) in 1981 put the total area of woodland on Exmoor as 6490 ha (9.3%)(STNC, 1981).

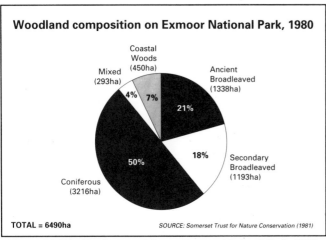

Woodland composition on Exmoor National Park, 1980

Coastal Woods (450ha)

Mixed (293ha) 4%

7%

Ancient Broadleaved (1338ha) 21%

18%

Secondary Broadleaved (1193ha)

Coniferous (3216ha) 50%

TOTAL = 6490ha

SOURCE: Somerset Trust for Nature Conservation (1981)

Figure 16 Woodland composition on Exmoor National Park, 1980.
Source: Somerset Trust for Nature Conservation (1981)

All three sources agree that half of the woodland area on Exmoor is coniferous. Beyond this however, it is the figures from the STNC (1981) that provide the most detailed indication of woodland composition on Exmoor (Figure 16). These figures are useful as they distinguish between secondary woodland (18% of cover) and ancient woodland, existing in 1600 (21% of cover). The proportion of ancient woodland on Exmoor is one of the largest of all the National Parks.

The distribution of woodland on Exmoor can be clearly located in four main groups (Figure 17). Each area raises its own particular issue for the NPA, who have a statutory duty to conserve and enhance the natural beauty of the Park as well as to promote public enjoyment. First, there are the broadleaved woodlands along the northern coast, composed of sessile oak, beech, ash, birch, sweet chestnut, hazel, alder and sycamore (Plate 29). Here there are some serious management problems concerning not only the neglected woodlands but also the stability of the coastal slopes. A study undertaken on Culbone Woods by a firm of consultants for the National Park indicated that the neglect of woodland management might be partly a cause of landslips in the area. It was suggested that regular cutting of coppice, which would have been the practice until about the Second World War, would have promoted a dense, rapidly transpiring crop to hold the unstable soil and to remove groundwater. With the neglect of coppicing, trees would have grown too heavy for the soils and slopes and generated small localised slips. It was recognised that while active woodland management might help to maintain stability of the slopes, a suitable technique for minimising debris erosion at the foot of the coastal slope was the primary solution (Integral Geotechnique Limited, 1992).

Plate 29 Coastal woodlands at Lynmouth.

Plate 30 Valley or combe woodland at Shillett Wood from Porlock Common.

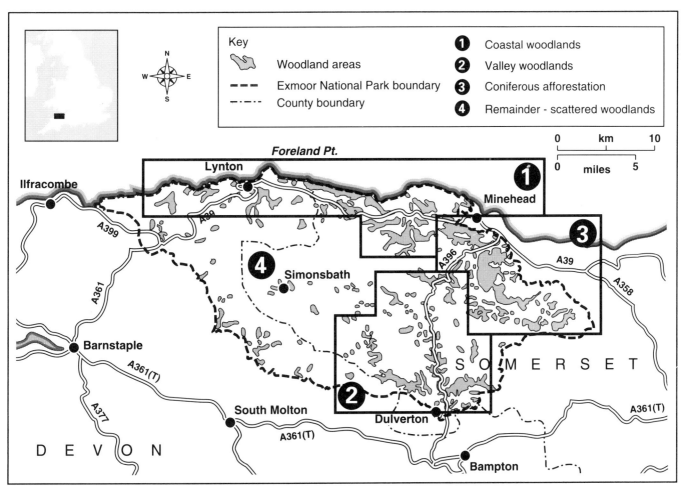

Figure 17 Generalised Woodland areas on Exmoor National Park.

The second group of woodlands on Exmoor is the valley, or combe, woodland systems in the south of the Park, which are particularly significant in both landscape and wildlife conservation terms (Plate 30). Many of these woodlands would have been managed under the coppice system in the past. The main issues for the National Park centre, first, on the problem of management neglect, as indicated by sycamore and rhododendron invasion and windblow, and, second, on how to find appropriate and economic means of managing the resource. This group of woodlands also contains the main remnants of ancient woodland (existing in 1600). Large areas of ancient woodland exist in the valleys of the Horner, Barle, Haddeo, Lyn, Hawkcombe, Exe and Quarme (STNC, 1981). Historical research by the STNC was able to show that ancient woodlands on Exmoor declined from 2295 ha in 1840 to 1338 ha in 1980 – a loss of 957 ha or 42%. Fortunately, most of the

73

ancient woods that survive lie in valleys on less reclaimable ground and are thus relatively contiguous. Further work by the STNC has indicated that many of the Exmoor ancient woodlands support nationally important communities of lichens (Wolseley and O'Dare, 1989). The main concern for the National Park is how to conserve these features as well as how to find the resources to do so.

The third distinct area of woodland on Exmoor is in the east of the Park where large-scale coniferous afforestation has occurred. These plantations are commercial and consist of Corsican pine, Sitka spruce, Norway spruce, Scots pine, Japanese larch, Douglas fir, cypress and Western hemlock. Although there has been a presumption against afforestation in the English uplands since 1988, the control of the extent, composition and design of coniferous plantations was a prime concern for the National Park until this time. Only about 11% of land capable of afforestation on Exmoor has been planted (Brotherton, 1983). The National Park is now attempting to assist the FC and private owners to promote increased diversity of species as many plantations reach the end of their first rotation and re-planting begins into the second rotation (Plate 31).

The fourth group of woodlands on Exmoor are the scattered woods, shelterbelts and beech-hedgerows that exist throughout the Park and which add so much diversity to the scenery. However, management issues have been raised about the maintenance of these landscape features (Plate 32). A study of hedgerows on Exmoor by Salter in 1977 showed that, while the scale and rate of hedgerow removal was comparatively small (about 320 km [200 miles] over the previous 20 years), the condition of many of the hedges was less than satisfactory (640 km [400 miles]) and required urgent attention if this feature of the landscape was to be maintained (Salter, 1977).

DEVELOPMENT OF WOODLAND POLICY IN THE EXMOOR NATIONAL PARK

The woodland management issues concerning the neglect of the broadleaved resource and the control of coniferous afforestation are of fundamental concern to the NPA for

Plate 31 Coniferous afforestation on Croydon Hill, showing felled and re-planted areas as the plantation enters its second rotation.

Exmoor. NPAs have a duty to maintain extensive areas of attractive natural and cultural landscapes for the preservation and enhancement of natural beauty. Woodlands have therefore formed a major part of the work and policies of NPAs. The means by which NPAs can influence the extent, composition and distribution of woodlands are through a mixture of encouragement and co-operation, such as agreements, grants and advice; compulsion, such as Tree Preservation Orders (TPOs) and felling licences; and by direct ownership and management. The role of NPAs with regard to woodlands is highly dependent on constructive liaison with private landowners and statutory agencies.

Previous research on the development of an NPA's policy for woodlands indicates that the process is far from rational and does not necessarily result in the implementation of the 'best' policy (Essex, 1990). Policy is often determined by internal factors, such as organisational arrangements and the influence of individuals, as well as external factors, such as the level of resources made available and the level of liaison and cooperation possible with other statutory agencies. Policy undergoes constant refinement based largely on experience derived from implementation and reaction to specific events or circumstances. This responsive nature of policy formulation

Plate 32 Mature beech tree hedgebanks on South Hill.
Over-maturity reduces the effectiveness of the shelter offered
by the hedgebanks.

what can be achieved from the system. The nature and evolution of the woodland policy of the Exmoor National Park follows a similar pattern, with a few significant differences. In addition, the study of changing management policies can be clearly related to the 'landscape signature' of woodlands and so is a research tool that ecologists and biogeographers might use in other contexts to help explain the character of woodlands.

Exmoor National Park was designated in 1954 and was run by a Joint Committee of Devon and Somerset County Councils until 1974. During this time, National Park management depended on officers of Somerset and Devon Council Councils based outside the National Park. After local government reorganisation, the National Park became the responsibility of a separate National Park Authority, with its own offices, staff and planning documents based at Dulverton inside the National Park. These institutional arrangements are fundamental in understanding the National Park's intervention in woodlands, especially in terms of the availability of dedicated personnel with responsibility for woodland management. Initially, woodlands were dealt with by the Woodland Officer of Somerset County Council in Taunton on the basis of approximately one day per week. This gives an important insight into the constraints on National Park intervention on woodlands for the first twenty years of the National Park's existence. With the creation of the ENPA with its own offices in Dulverton, the Park's own woodland officer was appointed in October 1974. In 1992, the woodland officer's post was changed to focus on management within ENPA owned woodlands while the post's woodland advisory role was transferred to a separate and newly created position.

Four incremental phases in the development of the woodland policy of the Exmoor National Park have been tentatively identified. The first phase occurred between 1954 and 1960 when the ENP was developing its role in response to afforestation proposals, particularly on the Chains. The second phase occurred between 1960 and 1974 when means of maintaining the broadleaved resource were developed. It was in this phase that a policy of purchase and direct management was adopted by the National Park. During the third phase, heralded by the creation of the separate NPA in 1974, there was

helps to explain the sometimes slow, conservative and almost opportunistic progression of intervention and indicates that radical policy prescription is often precluded. A consideration of these constraints is valuable since it places into perspective a re-evaluation of the role of the National Park in woodland purchase and management which clarified the National Park's involvement in woodlands. The management of the National Park's own woodland estate and the provision of advice to private woodland owners were the main activities established as a result of this review. Since 1985, a fourth phase might be identified, where there is increasing convergence in the interests of the ENPA, the Forestry Commission, English Nature, the Ministry of Agriculture, Fisheries and Food (MAFF) and other rural agencies. In 1994, the Exmoor NPA produced a Woodland Strategy to guide future management on Exmoor. The diversity of woodland landscapes bear the imprint or signature of these phases of evolving policy and shifts in management philosophy.

FIRST PHASE, 1954–1960: DEVELOPING ROLE

At its inception in 1954, Exmoor National Park Committee had limited controls over woodlands. First, landownership in National Parks remained largely with private individuals. Second, the role of National Parks with regard to woodland was subsidiary to that of the Forestry Commission (FC). The Dower Report (1945) had noted that the FC and National Parks were potentially rival claimants over large areas of upland country in which it was unlikely that both could operate successfully. It is possible that the FC considered that National Parks constituted obstacles to their aim for forestry expansion (MacEwen and MacEwen, 1982). Third, the National Park and Access to the Countryside Act of 1949 gave National Parks no extra controls over woodlands and forestry. Neither agricultural nor forestry developments were regarded as 'development' under the planning legislation introduced by the Town and Country Planning Act of 1947 and no changes were made to these arrangements for land in National Parks. National Parks therefore lacked effective controls over changes in the extent and composition of woodland.

In the 1950s, Exmoor was considered to be a viable location for coniferous afforestation by both the FC and private landowners. The minutes of the Exmoor National Park Joint Advisory Committee (ENPJAC), which first met on 29 July 1957, detail the deliberations concerning a number of FC proposals for afforestation in different parts of Exmoor. In most cases, the ENPJAC did not object to the planting proposals but instead suggested modifications to reduce the impact of the schemes on the Exmoor landscape, such as not planting on land above the 213m (700 feet) contour or on ancient monuments and by agreeing on the species of trees to be planted. However, in October 1957, the FC submitted proposals for the afforestation of about 400 ha (998 acres) on the Chains, near Simonsbath. This proposal posed a new problem for the Committee in that it was a scheme that would clearly damage an integral part of the scenery (and indeed essence) of the Moor. The committee expressed the view that the area concerned contained some of the most magnificent scenery in the Park; that it would be a tragedy to embark on planting schemes on such open areas; and that as a general principle no planting should be permitted on high ground on Exmoor as a whole (ENPJAC, 3.10.57). What was unclear was whether the views of the ENPJAC would be accepted by the FC and the issue became a well publicised national debate at the time (Bonham-Carter, 1991).

In dealing with the FC's proposal for the Chains and the need to find a compromise solution, the ENPJAC appointed a Forestry Sub-Committee not only to make recommendations about the proposals for the Chains but also to consider where and to what extent large scale afforestation might be undertaken on Exmoor without detriment to the purposes of the National Park (ENPJAC, 22.4.58). In the event, the FC proposals for The Chains were aborted following the death of Lord Fortescue, the owner of the land in 1958, and further representations made by the National Parks Commission (NPC) and ENPJAC to the FC (ENPJAC, 19.1.59). Consequently, it was the Sub-Committee's second objective, namely to establish a policy on the location and scale of all proposals, that was to be of longer standing importance to woodland policy on Exmoor and indeed within the UK. Between May and July, 1958 the entire area of the Park was surveyed by the Assistant Forestry Officer of Somerset County Council (Roger Miles) with a view to identifying areas of land where afforestation might be undertaken without detriment to the landscape (and LPA unlikely to oppose), areas where afforestation was thought to be undesirable (and LPA would oppose any afforestation proposal), and areas in which limited planting only might be acceptable in the landscape (and LPA would oppose if proposals unsuitable). This work became known as the Exmoor Afforestation Survey. The general principles of the scheme were presented to the ENPJAC in October, 1958. This meeting was also attended by a representative of the NPC, who commented on the constructive approach of the classification which had not yet been attempted in any other National Park (ENPJAC, 13.10.58). Specification of areas covered by the classifications were agreed by the Somerset Park Committee in April 1959 (ENPJAC, 20.4.59) and by the Devon Park Committee in July 1959 (ENPJAC, 27.7.59). Suggested modifications to the scheme by the NPC were not acted upon by the ENPJAC (ENPJAC 12.10.59), and the classifications were forwarded to the FC and MAFF for comment and agreement. The classification only applied to FC proposals but, by negotiation with the National Farmers' Union (NFU), Country Landowners' Association (CLA) and the Timber Growers' Organisation (TGO), private owners were also encouraged to follow the guidelines by April, 1961.

The involvement of the NPC in the Exmoor Afforestation classification influenced their advice and recommendations to other National Parks concerning forestry. First, the NPC asked all National Parks, including Exmoor, to consider the idea of establishing Voluntary Agreements over the location of afforestation in National Parks – very clearly based on the 'prototype' set up on Exmoor. Paradoxically, Exmoor even had to slightly modify its own original and existing scheme to respond to this external pressure which caused critical comment from certain quarters. There were concerns that the new agreement did not reflect the spirit of the original Exmoor scheme. Consultations particularly over the wording of categories of Exmoor's Voluntary Agreement for Afforestation took until 1971 (Figure 18).

The second proposal made by the NPC to help NPAs control afforestation was to set up Forestry Consultative Panels. These panels were to include representatives from the National Park, FC, CLA, TGO and Nature Conservancy and were to advise the National Park and FC on matters of mutual interest, such as proposals by the FC to acquire land in National Parks,

proposals for clearfelling in private woods and major afforestation schemes. The idea was not well received on Exmoor as it was thought to duplicate and even reduce the influence of the existing National Park Committee and that existing arrangements for consultation were adequate (ENPJAC, 8.3.63).

SECOND PHASE, 1960–1974: CONCERN FOR BROADLEAVED WOODS

While the first phase was almost exclusively concerned with establishing the means of controlling coniferous afforestation, the second phase started to devote increasing attention to maintaining the broadleaved resource. The formation of the Exmoor Society, a public group established as a response to The Chains incident with the intention of protecting the local scene, acted to raise awareness of this issue. One of the aims of the Society was to encourage the management of broadleaved woodlands as amenity features (ENPJAC, 27.7.59). The experience of the National Park in responding to emerging issues also provided a stimulus to intervention in protecting the broadleaved resource of Exmoor. During the early 1960s, there were a number of proposals received for consideration by ENPJAC for the conversion of existing broadleaved woodlands into coniferous forests by forestry companies and syndicates and through the FC's Dedication Scheme. In order that the ENPJAC might be in a position to conserve broadleaved woodlands in the landscape, it was decided that a survey should be prepared of all areas of woodland considered of special landscape importance (ENPJAC, 11.4.60). A list of woodlands of Special Scenic Importance was produced for the Committee Meeting in July 1960 (ENPJAC, 11.7.60) (Figure 19). In later meetings it was considered whether TPOs should be designated for all woods on this list as it was the only means by which control could be exercised over the woodland areas by the ENPJAC (ENPJAC, 11.10.60). It was also realised that designation of a TPO on a woodland did not necessarily secure its protection.

On occasions the National Park would make small financial payments, by way of compensation, to landowners who

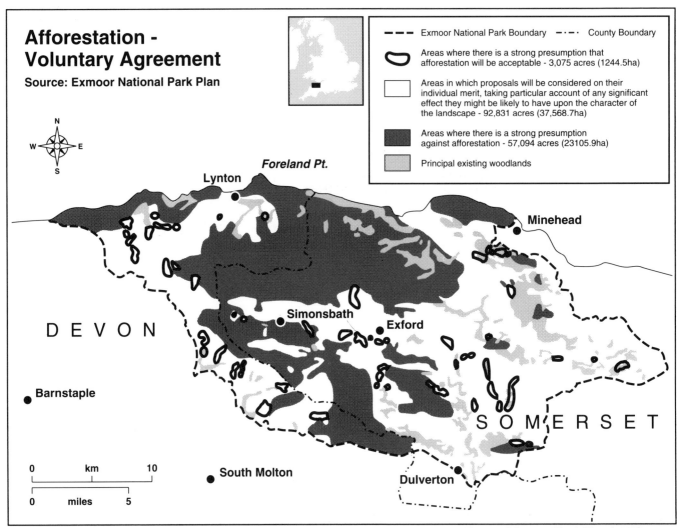

Figure 18 Voluntary agreement for afforestation in Exmoor National Park, 1971. Source: Exmoor National Park Plan *(1977).*

modified their planting schemes to accord with National Park wishes. By January 1961, this approach began to give way to the realisation that purchase of the woodland by the National Park might be the most effective means of achieving woodland conservation. It was decided that 'if no agreement can be reached on a method of management which will retain its existing character with or without financial assistance, that consideration be given to acquiring the wood' (ENPJAC, 16.1.61). This decision is mirrored by developments in other National Parks at about the same time but was supported by

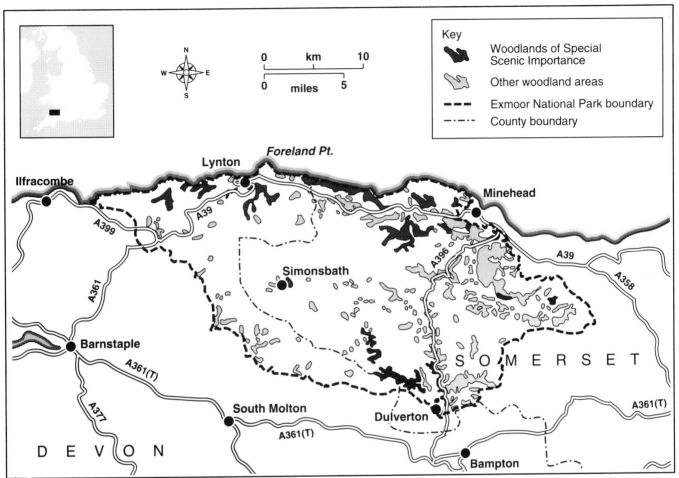

Figure 19 Woodlands of Special Scenic Importance, 1960. Source: ENPJAC Minutes, 11.7.60.

generous financial allocations from Somerset County Council. Exmoor proceeded to purchase more woodland than any other National Park and now has a woodland estate of 425 ha (i.e. about 5% of woodlands in the National Park). In comparison the FC and National Trust (NT) each own about 20% of Exmoor's woodlands, the Crown a further 5% while private owners own the remaining 50% (ENPA, 1991).

THIRD PHASE, 1974–1985: RE-EVALUATION AND STRENGTHENING ROLE

The creation of the new ENPA in 1974, prompted a more cautious attitude towards further acquisition of woods. There was a realisation that unquestioning growth of the National Park's woodland estate without the resources to purchase or manage the woodlands adequately would be unwise. In order to guide the ENPA in its future woodland policy a consultant, Peter Garthwaite, was employed to give specialist opinion. His report, published in 1977, contained three main conclusions. First, there was a clear recommendation that the ENPA should continue to accept more woodlands into its ownership despite concerns about adequate resourcing for purchase and management. In the author's view it was desirable that the ENPA should own and manage a considerable proportion of woodland in the Park in order to achieve its objectives and that opportunities to acquire particular woods might never recur once refused.

Second, the need for planned management of the ENPA's woodlands was stressed and, in particular, the introduction of shelterwood silvicultural systems was recommended to maintain continuous tree cover in the Authority's woodlands. Other features of management such as the importance of diversifying the structure of the woods, of thinning, of removing rhododendron and encouraging public access to the woods were discussed. Treatment proposals were detailed for the different types of woodland under the National Park's ownership and three levels of priorities were established. Top priority was given to areas urgently needing woodland management (40ha) and largely referred to thinning operations in one particular ageing woodland (Hawkcombe Wood). The second level of priority was given to mature woodlands that required selective felling to enable the shelterwood system to be introduced (e.g. Birch Cleave near Simonsbath and Woodcombe Brake above Minehead) (102ha). The remaining area of woodland (244ha) was given the lowest priority and included some woodlands that were either beyond redemption (e.g. some oak coppice areas) or on steep slopes (parts of the coastal woods). Cutting across all priorities was the need for rhododendron removal in nearly all the ENPA's woods, which was reducing the wildlife potential of the woods but would require a colossal investment to physically remove the plants.

The third recommendation made by Garthwaite concerned the resourcing of such management. It was estimated that a minimum annual allocation for labour of £40 per ha was required for the present holding and for any future acquisitions. On this basis, employment could be provided for five people. It was also pointed out that costs could be recouped by an increasing income from the sale of produce resulting from management.

The recommendations of this report have been implemented slowly. Although further woodland has been acquired since Garthwaite's report, by 1994, only 39 ha had been added to the 1977 total. Management plans have been formulated for many of the ENPA's woodlands, clearly stating the operations required to maintain and enhance the landscape, wildlife conservation and recreation value of the woods. In each of these plans, systematic consideration is given to the background of the wood and the woodland and access management issues involved. They also include detailed management prescriptions with associated financial implications as well as a series of maps illustrating the location of compartments and issues. By 1994, the National Park had a team of 17 estate workers, who worked on woodland management (as well as other estate management duties), together with a depot and sawmill. The Park is now self-sufficient in timber used in park management. A lot of the more straight-forward woodland management work is also undertaken on a contract basis and the ENPA has been generous in the allocation of resources to this budget. In 1981/82, about £2,500 was allocated for contract services which increased to £7,500 in 1982/83 (ENPA, 19.10.82) and to approximately £27,000 in 1993/94 (D. Wood, Pers. Comm., 1994).

In response to the need for resources for woodland management, the ENPA launched the 'Woodland Conservation Fund' in November 1983, in order to raise money, by public subscription, to assist in conservation management of woodland in the National Park (ENPA 25.11.83). By October 1984, the Fund had raised £5,620 (ENPA 16.10.84). In the mid 1980s the Fund became a free standing trust and by March 1988 had received charitable status and raised about £13,000. The Fund's monies are available to assist public and private woodland owners to maintain Exmoor woods. Although there have been criticisms in the press that the Fund has been hijacked by hunting interests (ENPA, 3.3.87), the scheme itself does represent another innovative approach to woodland management on Exmoor. Similarly, the staging of Woodland

Craft weeks since 1988 raises public awareness of local produce and alerts woodland craft businesses to the benefits of woodland management. Four events have been staged between 1988 and 1994.

FOURTH PHASE, 1985–PRESENT: GREATER CONVERGENCE

Since the mid-1980s the raised environmental awareness of other rural agencies, such as the FC and MAFF, has been of considerable benefit to the woodland management work of the ENPA. New schemes and initiatives have encouraged an increasing convergence of interests between the statutory bodies. The introduction of the Broadleaved Woodland Grant Scheme by the FC in 1985 not only freed up some of the National Park's resources to be used on other activities but also meant that the National Park could itself apply for grant aid from this source. The Wildlife and Countryside Act 1985 led to the preparation of Section 3 maps for National Parks, which identified areas that were particularly important to conserve for their natural beauty. Other agencies had to honour these classifications in their activities. A total of 5000 ha of woodland has been included on the Section 3 Conservation Map.

Changes in Government forestry policy in 1988, preventing afforestation on land over 244m (800 feet), meant that the Voluntary Agreement for Afforestation 1971 ceased to be relevant on Exmoor. Nevertheless, an interim Woodland Agreement between the ENPA, FC, Timber Growers UK and CLA was set up in 1991 to establish a basis for maintaining the existing landscape cover in valued areas and considering all new planting proposals on their merits elsewhere, with a presumption in favour of broadleaved and mixed planting schemes which contribute to landscape and wildlife interests (ENPA, 1991). An Environmentally Sensitive Area (ESA) designation for Exmoor in 1992 provided extra resources for hedgerow management, amongst other assistance. The ENPA itself is also continuing to be forward looking in its approach to woodland management. During 1994, a Woodland Strategy was prepared to guide the work of the ENPA in woodland conservation. The strategy includes an action plan and identifies six key areas for future attention. These include

continued attempts to remove rhododendrons from woodlands on Exmoor; the targeting of the ENPAs woodland activities on problem issues or areas (e.g. encourage more natural regeneration as opposed to new planting); the development of markets for products from Exmoor woodlands; the incorporation of the Interim Woodland Agreement 1991 concerning locations for planting; and the development of a Geographical Information System (GIS) database for woodland resource and management on Exmoor. This strategy provides clear direction for the National Park's woodland work and for the first time sets out clear objectives which can be judged by outcomes within a determined timescale.

CONCLUSION

The woodland resource on Exmoor has developed as a result of a number of influences, both physical and human. It has been human intervention that has played the decisive role in determining the extent, composition and geography of the woodlands. The upland clearance of woodland in prehistoric times, the pattern of agriculture in the Saxon period, the landscaping of estates in the eighteenth century, the land reclamation in the nineteenth century and the coniferous afforestation in the twentieth century have all left their mark on the Exmoor woodland scene. The designation of Exmoor as a National Park in 1954, in recognition of the area's unique landscape character, has introduced another influence on the development of woodlands in the area. The shifts in the ENPA's woodland policy can be identified in the landscapes of the Park, particularly in terms of controlling the worst excesses of coniferous afforestation and ensuring broadleaved conservation. The National Park has emerged as an important agency in woodland conservation and management on Exmoor and has achieved a great deal.

In particular, the National Park has developed a woodland policy, formulated through systematic and careful consideration. The Exmoor Afforestation Survey of 1958 provided the foundation for the policy for dealing with proposals for coniferous afforestation, while the identification of woodlands of Special Scenic Importance in 1960 and the Garthwaite study in 1977 assisted in the conservation and management of broadleaved woodlands. The Woodland Strategy of 1994 represents the most recent stage in the systematic development of woodland policy and intervention on Exmoor.

The forms of policy intervention that have been introduced to deal with woodland issues on Exmoor have been appropriate and generally effective. Coniferous afforestation, which was a major threat in the 1950s, was controlled by the establishment of a Voluntary Afforestation Agreement with the FC and, later, with other forestry interests. This approach was pioneered on Exmoor and was later taken as the model for adoption by other National Parks in England and Wales. Broadleaved woodland conservation and management has been effected through the purchase and management of woodlands by the ENPA. The purchases have enabled the ENPA to develop and practise exemplary woodland management practices and approaches and the potential for the ENPA's woods to become income generators through the production and marketing of woodland products is significant.

However, the effectiveness of these two main approaches is very much dependent on the goodwill of woodland owners and the availability of sufficient resources. Both these factors lie outside the National Park's control and represent a dilemma for National Park management. Voluntary Agreements, while providing some form of control, can be difficult to enforce particularly in changed circumstances. Purchase and management of woodlands by the National Park, while appearing to be more direct, is limited by available finance and labour. Even more potentially self-sustaining approaches, such as the marketing of local woodland produce to stimulate management, have enormous implications for the ENPA's limited resources. The removal of rhododendrons from Exmoor woodlands is another immediate priority for the ENPA that is held back by lack of resources. Given these constraints, the National Park's woodland intervention over the last 40 years must be viewed as making many advances in woodland management and conservation. It is difficult to suggest how the National Park could have acted and developed a woodland policy along any other lines. What is clear, however, is that the challenges of woodland management and conservation will become ever more demanding in the future.

ACKNOWLEDGEMENTS

The author would like to thank David Wood (Exmoor National Park Senior Estates Officer) and Sarah Menear (Exmoor National Park Landscape Officer) for their valuable assistance in the writing of this chapter. Thanks also to Drs Brayshay and Gibb for their comments on a draft of this chapter, Brian Rogers and Tim Absalom for the cartography, Suzanne Brodie for the typing and Lyn and Bob for their hospitality on Exmoor.

REFERENCES

V. Bonham-Carter, *The Essence of Exmoor*, (Dulverton, 1991) 62-79.

I. Brotherton, 'Determinants of Landscape Change: The Case of Afforestation in the National Parks of England and Wales', *Landscape Planning*, 9, (1983) 193-207.

Centre for Agricultural Strategy, 'Strategy for the UK Forest Industry', *CAS Report No.6*, (Reading, 1980).

G. Court, *Exmoor National Park*, (Exeter,1987).

L. Curtis, 'Exmoor', in W.S.Lacey, (ed.) *Britain's National Parks*, (Leicester, 1984) 31-41.

H.C.Darby & R. Welldon-Finn, (eds.) *The Domesday Geography of South-West England*, (Cambridge, 1967) 172-179.

J. Dower, *National Parks in England and Wales*, (London, 1945).

R. Edwards, *Fit for the Future: Report of the National Parks Review Panel*, (Cheltenham, 1991).

S.J.Essex, 'Woodland planning in the Peak District National Park: Formulation and implementation of a land use policy', *Land Use Policy*, 7, No. 3, (1990) 243-256.

Exmoor National Park Joint Advisory Committee (ENPJAC) *Committee Minutes*, (Dulverton, 1957-1974).

Exmoor National Park Authority (ENPA) *Committee Minutes,* (Dulverton, 1974).

ENPA, *Exmoor National Park Plan,* (Dulverton, 1977) 31-35.

ENPA, *Exmoor National Park Plan Review,* (Dulverton, 1983) W(i) - W(ix).

ENPA *Exmoor National Park Plan, 1991-1996,* (Dulverton, 1991) 29-34.

ENPA, *Management Plan for Birchcleave Wood,* (Dulverton, 1990).

ENPA, *Management Plan for Dulverton Woodlands,* (Dulverton, 1990).

ENPA, *Management Plan for Hawkcombe Woods,* (Dulverton, undated).

A.Hobhouse, *National Parks in England and Wales,* (London, 1947).

P. Garthwaite, *Woodlands in the Exmoor National Park,* (Dulverton, 1977).

Integral Geotechnique Limited, *Study of Landslipped Coastal Slopes and Woodland: Culbone Woods, Somerset,* (Bristol, 1992).

K. Kirby, G. Peterken, J. Spencer and G. Walker, *Inventories of Ancient Semi-natural Woodland,* (Peterborough, 1984).

J.A. Lister and A.L.Pinches, *Devon Inventory of Ancient Woodlands,* (Peterborough, 1986).

A & M. MacEwen, *National Parks: Conservation or Cosmetics?,* (London, 1982).

R.Miles, *The Trees and Woods of Exmoor,* (Dulverton, 1972).

C.S.Orwin and R.J.Sellick, *The Reclamation of Exmoor Forest,* 2nd Revised Ed., (Newton Abbot, 1970).

B. Salter, *Beech Hedgerow Study,* (Dulverton, 1978).

P.A.Wolseley and A.M. O'Dare, *Exmoor Woodlands: Lichens Survey,1987-88,* (Bridgwater, 1989).

Somerset Trust For Nature Conservation, *Exmoor Woodland Survey: A Survey of Ancient Woodland in the Exmoor National Park,* (Bridgwater, 1981).

THE CHANGING LANDSCAPE OF EXMOOR: NATIONAL PARK MONITORING AND MANAGEMENT USING GEOGRAPHICAL INFORMATION SYSTEMS

Andrew R. Harrison and Richard Dunn

Department of Geography, University of Bristol

INTRODUCTION

Earlier chapters in this book have considered landscape change in Exmoor over the past 10,000 years and beyond. Here the emphasis is on contemporary change; to be specific, the monitoring of changes in land cover and related landscape features that have occurred in Exmoor over the past twenty five years. In addition, this chapter will also consider how information on landscape change is being used within computer-based information systems to assist in the management of the National Park.

To address these themes, this chapter draws extensively on the outcomes of two projects which have separately considered the two main issues associated with monitoring landscape change: data collection and data use.

The first, the Monitoring Landscape Change in the National Parks (MLCNP) project, provided a complete survey of land cover in the National Parks in England and Wales based on the interpretation of aerial photographs acquired in the 1970s and the late 1980s (Countryside Commission & Countryside Council for Wales, 1991). The second, and more recent, project has investigated the use of the MLCNP data set, in conjunction with other environmental data sets, in order to make full use of the information for Park management and monitoring. This work has focused on the potential use of computer-based information technology, in particular the application of Geographical Information Systems (GIS), for the handling and analysis of landscape data (Dunn and Harrison, 1993, 1995).

The chapter starts by providing some background to the MLCNP project and then goes on to describe how the project was organised and how the data were collected. Both the way the survey was organised and the methods used strongly influenced the characteristics of the data collected, their limitations and ultimately how they can be used. Results from the MLCNP project are then considered. In particular, the MLCNP data for Exmoor are presented to show how the landscape of Exmoor has changed in recent years. Finally, some examples from recent work on Exmoor in which GIS are being used to analyse the MLC data are given.

BACKGROUND

The passage through Parliament of the Wildlife and Countryside Act in the early 1980s and the debate which the Act engendered focused attention on the ways in which the character and appearance of the countryside have been altering and are likely to be affected in the future by changes in farming, forestry and other economic land uses. In recent decades, some of these changes have accelerated, and they have attracted increasing public notice. For example, urban encroachment on the countryside, major developments such as new roads and motor ways, rail terminals and airports, the removal of hedgerows, the drainage of wetlands, the conversion of heather moorland to grassland and of broad-leaf woodland to coniferous plantation. As a result there is widespread debate about existing policies for the countryside.

At the same time, this debate has highlighted the inadequacies of the statistics upon which many of the assertions about landscape change rest. Although there are national figures for some, e.g. the loss of agricultural land to urban development, much of the information comes from local or regional surveys which are often not representative of the national pattern of change.

In order to address this lack of consistent and reliable information, in 1984 the DOE and Countryside Commission commissioned a two year project to monitor changes in the landscape of England and Wales (Huntings Technical Services, 1986). To do this, aerial photography from around 1947, 1969 and 1980 was used to interpret and measure the extent of landscape features at a sample of sites. The survey, which was completed two years later in 1986, showed that over the post-war period (1947-80) losses of farmed land to built-up land were mainly from improved grassland. Gains to farmed land were mainly from semi-natural vegetation and broadleaved woodland while cultivated land increased chiefly at the expense of improved grassland. Most new coniferous woodlands were previously broadleaved woodland or upland grass.

A repeat MLC survey was planned but never took place although the joint DOE/ITE Countryside Survey, carried out in 1990 and which reported last year, has provided more up-to-date information on how the landscape is changing (DOE, 1993).

From the standpoint of the National Parks, the basic problem with these existing data sets is that they say very little about how the landscape within the Parks is altering. Both MLC and

Countryside Survey 1990 were sample-based surveys designed solely to provide statistically reliable estimates of landscape change at national level. A different approach for the National Parks was required.

THE MLCNP PROJECT

The MLCNP project was commissioned in 1987 by the Countryside Commission, the National Park Authorities and the Broads Authority, and was carried out by Silsoe College over the period 1988-1991 (Silsoe College, 1991). The broad objective was for a comprehensive survey to monitor recent landscape change in the National Parks and to provide a baseline against which future change could be assessed.

While the MLCNP project was established as a joint exercise between the Countryside Commission and all the Park authorities, the Commission took a lead role throughout the project based on the need for a consistent baseline survey across all the National Parks. The summary report was published in 1991 jointly by the Countryside Commission and the Countryside Council for Wales (CCW). (From 1 April 1991 the CCW had become the agency concerned with the interests of the National Parks in Wales) (Countryside Commission and Countryside Council for Wales, 1991).

There were two important consequences of this project organisation. Firstly, a single classification scheme, based on a standard set of land cover definitions, was used for the survey. Whilst considerable efforts were made to accommodate the specific, and in some cases unique, landscape features and habitats of each National Park into the classification scheme, the result was inevitably a compromise which reduced the potential use of the data in a number of the Parks. The MLCNP classification scheme is shown in Table 4.

Secondly, and related to this previous point, the strong lead given by the Countryside Commission and the use of external contractors cultivated a view that the survey was more about meeting the information requirements of the parent organisation than providing a data set that each NP would

Classification of Land Cover and Landscape Features

A Linear Features	A1 Hedgerows	
	A2 Fences and insubstantial field boundaries	
	A3 Walls	
	A4 Banks	
	A5 Open ditches	
	A6 Woodland edge	
	A8 Strip woodland	
	A9 Grips	
B Small or Isolated Features	B1 Individual trees in linear features	
	B2 Individual trees outside linear features	
	B3 Groups of trees, all species	
	B6 Inland water	
C Wood and Forest Land	C1 Broadleaved high forest	
	C2 Coniferous high forest	
	C3 Mixed high forest	
	C4 Scrub	
	C5 Clear felled/newly planted areas	
D Moor and Heath Land	D1 Upland heath	
	D2 Upland grass moor	(b) grass moor
		(d) blanket peat grass moor
	D3 Bracken	
	D4 Unenclosed lowland areas	(a) rough grassland
		(b) heath
	D6 Upland mosaics	(a) heath/grass
		(b) heath/bracken
		(c) heath/blanket peat
	D7 Eroded areas	(a) peat
		(b) mineral soils
	D8 Coastal heath	
E Agro-pastoral Land	E1 Cultivated land	
	E2 Grassland	(a) improved pasture
		(b) rough pasture
F Water and Wetland	F1 Open water, coastal	
	F2 Open water, inland	
	F3 Wetland vegetation	(a) peat bog
		(b) freshwater marsh
		(c) saltmarsh
G Rock and Coastal Land	G2 Bare rock	(a) inland
		(b) coastal
	G3 Other coastal features	(a) dunes
		(b) sand beach
		(c) shingle beach
		(d) mud flats
H Developed Land	H1 Built-up land	(a) urban area
		(b) major transport route
	H2 Quarries, mineral workings and derelict land	(a) quarries and mineral working
		(b) derelict land
	H3 Isolated rural developments	(a) farmsteads (>0.25 ha)
		(b) other (>0.25 ha)
I Unclassified Land		

Table 4 Classification of land cover and landscape features used in the MLCNP survey.

adopt for its own use. In addition, at that time, virtually all of the Parks were without the technical means, in terms of appropriate GIS hardware and software, to handle the MLCNP data. It is not surprising therefore, that, to date, the data have been little used within the NPs themselves and, as a consequence, have had little impact on NP management and policy evaluation.

THE METHOD OF MONITORING

A specific requirement of the MLCNP survey was the ability to derive statistical and mapped information on the extent, distribution and change over time of the wide range of land cover types occurring in the National Parks. The approach adopted was broadly similar to that used in the MLC project of England and Wales two years earlier, being based on airphoto interpretation (API), linked to limited ground survey for field

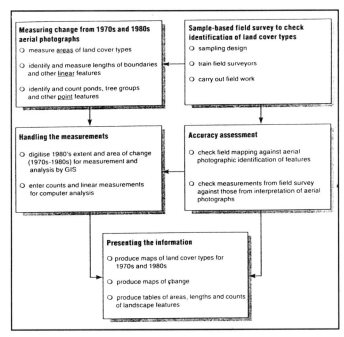

Figure 20 Relationship between elements of the MLCNP survey method.

checking purposes. The method developed for the MLCNP survey is summarised in Figure 20.

The main data source for the survey was aerial photography. Aerial photographs covering the whole of each Park, taken in the 1970s and late 1980s, were compared in order to identify the changes that had taken place between these two dates. Aerial photography for Exmoor comprised existing black and white photographs acquired between 1971-75 and black and white and 70 mm true colour photographs acquired specifically for the MLCNP survey in 1989. The aerial photography was then interpreted according to the land cover and landscape feature definitions in the classification scheme. Here the use of the classification scheme was crucial as it not only determined where the interpreter drew boundaries on the aerial photographs but also, in relation to how well the interpreter could identify the features, determined the accuracy of the resulting data.

Three broad categories of landscape feature were identified: area features (e.g. woodlands and moorland), linear features (e.g. hedgerows and fences) and point features (e.g. individual trees and ponds). The boundary of each area feature was stored in the computer. For the point and linear features, counts and linear measurements were recorded for each 1 km square within the Park.

The main objective of the field surveys was to check the accuracy of the API although it also assisted in the interpretation of certain features in the aerial photography itself. To check the accuracy of the API a sample of 1 km squares was visited and mapped in the field. The field surveyed squares were then compared with the same area mapped by API which enabled a quantitative estimate of the interpretation accuracy for each landscape feature. Overall agreement between field survey data and API in Exmoor was 86%. This increased to 95% overall accuracy at the level of main classes (categories A-I in Table 4). Possible sources of error in the MLCNP data are discussed in more detail below.

Once the maps and measurements had been converted into a

computer-compatible form and checked, the final stage of the method involved analysis of the data to present statistical summaries and information about change. To facilitate comparison between the 1970s and 1980s the area feature data were overlaid with a 20 m x 20 m grid. The code for each area feature was then allocated to the appropriate grid cell. This produced a data set comprising a land cover code for the 1970s and a land cover code for the 1980s for every 20 m square within each park.

An important difference between the MLCNP project and its predecessor, the MLC survey of England and Wales, was that it was a census of land cover rather than referring to just a limited number of sample sites. In other words, in the MLCNP project the entire land surface of each NP was mapped, to an equivalent scale of 1:10,000, and classified according to a set of detailed land cover definitions. This provides significant advantages over the sample-based approach making it possible to use the data at the level of the Park as a whole or any other user-defined area down to individual land parcels or features.

SOURCES OF ERROR

Having reviewed the methods used in collecting and analysing the MLCNP data, and before going on to look at the results of the survey, a number of practical limitations, arising from possible sources of error in the data, need to be borne in mind. While the method used was designed to minimise these sources of error it is inevitable that some will occur.

Errors were possible from three sources: in identifying landscape features from aerial photographs, in measuring the number or length of features or in digitising boundaries and in the handling and analysis of the information.

The largest source of error arises from the practical difficulties of using aerial photographs and correctly identifying landscape features from them. Practical difficulties stem from the limitations and constraints of the available photography (e.g. cloud cover, steep terrain and shadow resulted in missing data;

photographic scale and timing of acquisition added to the difficulties of consistent interpretation). In Exmoor National Park the 1970s coverage was taken over three years in four different months. Some changes could have occurred within the time span of the data while the changing appearance of vegetation through the annual growth cycle made it difficult to achieve equally consistent interpretations of certain cover types in photographs acquired in different months. For example, on Exmoor bracken could be clearly identified in the June 1989 photography, due to the availability of the 70 mm colour photography which identified areas of new growth. However, in the May and June 1970s black and white photography it was difficult to distinguish this new growth. There was also a significant difference in image quality between the 1970s and 1980s photography. The relatively inferior quality of the 1980s photography made identification of linear features difficult.

Interpretation difficulties are due not only to the characteristics of the available photography but also relate to the task of applying a set of definitions in order to classify a particular piece of terrain. For example, on Exmoor, difficulties arose in distinguishing Upland Grass Moor from Rough Pasture, due to the patterns of enclosure, and also Improved from Rough Pasture. There were particular problems associated with the identification of linear features. For example, trimmed and laid hedgerows were sometimes confused with walls or well maintained banks. As this last example shows, care must be taken when interpreting the results from the MLCNP survey. In this particular case, it is likely that the change statistics for Exmoor's hedges and banks reflect the system of management as well as actual losses of hedgerows or gains in banks.

With these methodological and data quality issues in mind it is now possible to look at the MLCNP data and to see what they reveal about recent landscape change in Exmoor.

THE CHANGING LANDSCAPE OF EXMOOR

An important feature of the MLCNP project was the use of a GIS to store and manipulate the landscape change data. A GIS is a computer-based information system which is designed to manipulate geographical data, and which has four key capabilities: (i) data capture, (ii) data storage, (iii) data analysis and (iv) data display. In plainer words, a GIS will accept geographical data (maps and associated data) in some computer-compatible form (data capture), store and analyse those data, and then produce graphical images of the data, typically in the form of maps (data display). Statistical summaries may also be derived from GIS analysis in the form of tables and other statistical or business graphics.

The sequence of maps on the colour pages were produced by a GIS. The maps were composed virtually instantaneously by computer and demonstrate the potential of holding the data in digital form enabling maps for any area and any set of categories to be displayed rapidly. Note the gridded format of the data which was explained earlier.

Figure 21 (colour section) shows a summary map of the main land cover types on Exmoor in the 1980s. The high central moorland plateau is clearly visible, the grass moorland of the former Royal Forest surrounded by commons of heather moorland. To the east is the extensive farmland of the Vale of Porlock. The following two Figures show the main categories 'Moor and Heath Land' and 'Woodland' mapped according to their constituent types. Figure 22 (colour section) shows the main category 'Moor and Heath Land' mapped according to its seven constituent types. Figure 23 (colour section) shows the main category 'Woodland' mapped according to its five constituent types.

Presenting the landscape change data as a series of maps enables overall patterns and trends to be identified. It provides a powerful way of summarising the data and enabling the analyst to focus into specific areas and to customise the map in response to specific questions. This use of GIS as an interactive and dynamic map analysis tool is one of the main advantages of using this approach. However, this type of approach translates less well to the printed page and it should be borne in mind that many benefits relate to this graphical and exploratory approach to data analysis.

In order to extract more quantitative information about landscape change in Exmoor it is more appropriate and effective here to use more conventional forms of graphical display. Again all the analysis designed to derive the statistical information presented here was produced by the GIS, although the graphics themselves have been redrawn for reasons of clarity in this book.

Just before presenting this graphical analysis of landscape change in Exmoor it is necessary to provide some explanation of the different ways of expressing land cover change. Change can be expressed in two ways, either as net or gross change. Net change is the difference in the total area of land in the 1970s and the 1980s and is based on the areal totals for that class. Gross change is a measure of the total movement from or to a land cover class between the 1970s and the 1980s, and is based on the total area lost or gained in that class. Net change is therefore a measure of overall loss or gain while gross change is a measure of the dynamics of the landscape features.

Figure 24 shows net changes in the Exmoor landscape between the 1970s and 1980s. Note that the changes have taken place over a 15-18 year period, given the dates of the Exmoor aerial photography. There was little overall change in broadleaved

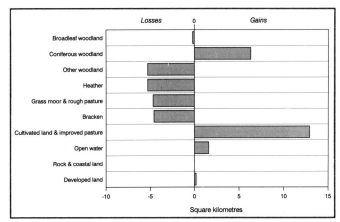

Figure 24 Overall gains and losses in land cover types in Exmoor from the 1970s to the 1980s (sq. km).

woodland, improved pasture, coastal land and areas of development.

There was an overall increase in cultivated land (gained from improved pasture), coniferous forest (gained mainly from clear felled/newly planted land, and open water (gained mainly from pasture).

There was an overall decrease in upland heath (lost mainly to heath mosaic), grass moor and rough pasture (lost mainly to improve pasture), and bracken (lost mainly to pasture and scrub).

Figure 25 shows gross changes in the Exmoor landscape between the 1970s and 1980s. There was considerable movement into and out of all types of enclosed farmland, all types of moor and heath, clear felled/newly planted land, and coniferous forest

Figure 26 summarises the changes, both net and gross, in enclosed farmland in Exmoor between the 1970s and 1980s. Note that the dominant direction of change was from rough pasture to improved pasture to cultivated land, with a lesser degree of reversion in the other direction.

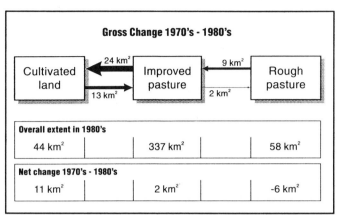

Figure 26 Changes (net and gross) in enclosed farmland in Exmoor between the 1970s to the 1980s (sq. km).

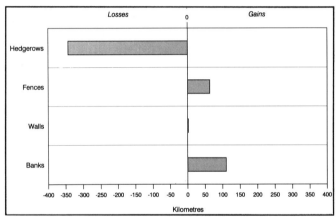

Figure 27 Changes in field boundaries in Exmoor from the 1970s to the 1980s (km).

Having considered change in areal landscape features it is possible, using a similar approach, to use the MLCNP data to analyse changes in linear landscape features. Figure 27 shows changes in field boundaries from the 1970s to the 1980s. The graph shows an overall increase in length of fences. However, the loss of 343 km or 11% of its 1970s total of hedgerows is exaggerated. This is due to the difficulties of differentiating between hedgerows and banks in the aerial photographs.

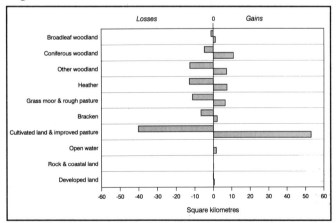

Figure 25 Areas gained to and lost from each land cover type in Exmoor from the 1970s to the 1980s (sq. km).

On Exmoor, banks often have hedges growing along their tops. These are periodically cut back to their bases. When mature, the bank was obscured by the hedge when viewed from the air and was therefore recorded as a hedge. When cut, however, there was often no visible trace of the hedge and the linear was recorded as a bank. The results show a decline in hedgerows, accompanied by an apparent increase in banks and this almost certainly results from this difficulty of interpretation. If the hedgerows and banks are combined then the loss was of the order of 5% which was commensurate with hedgerow loss in the other NPs.

In summary, three general points can be made based on this brief review of the results from the MLCNP survey for Exmoor.

Firstly, the monitoring study has resulted in the first ever comprehensive census of landscape features in the National Parks. Given the format of the data set it can be manipulated and presented in a rapid and flexible manner.

Secondly, and drawing on the results of the survey, it appears that in many respects the landscape of Exmoor has changed little. There has, however, been a move to more intensive management with an overall increase in the area of cultivated land, improved pasture and coniferous forest and in the length of fences. These changes have been inevitably accompanied by a total decrease in the more traditional features of the landscape.

Thirdly, and again drawing on the results of the survey, the nature of landscape change is complex with significant levels of movement within and between different types of land cover. This is particularly evident in different types of enclosed farmland, forestry (newly planted/clear felled/coniferous forest), and the various types of moor and heath.

MANAGING LANDSCAPE CHANGE: THE USE OF GIS

The remaining part of this chapter reviews more recent work which has investigated the wider use of GIS within the context of the day-to-day work of the National Parks. This work stemmed from the wishes of the Countryside Commission and the National Park Authorities to explore the potential of the MLCNP data set and possibilities for enhancing it, in order to make full use of the information for policy making and for Park management and monitoring. The project title was 'Monitoring Landscape Change in the National Parks: Information and Advisory Service for the Southern Parks' and involved Exmoor and Dartmoor National Parks and the Broads Authority. Only those aspects of the project concerned with Exmoor National Park are considered here.

As the title implies the work involved working closely with staff in each of the Parks. The project explored the potential for the use of GIS within the National Park by developing a series of demonstration projects. The aim was to enable parks to develop an awareness of the potential of GIS, by providing practical insights into the implementation and organisational issues of setting-up and running a GIS, whilst avoiding any commitment to the technology in the first instance. The basis of the approach was that each GIS demonstrator be user-centred and user-led to ensure that the topics chosen for detailed analysis reflected the priorities and needs of the National Park. Accordingly, the project placed considerable emphasis on liaison with users and familiarisation with related projects, with a series of meetings taking place before any development work was undertaken.

Early meetings relating to Exmoor indicated that there had been almost no use of the MLCNP data within the National Park and that there was some scepticism about the value and accuracy of the data set. Given earlier comments about the organisation of the MLCNP project, this was not surprising and was exacerbated by the fact that Exmoor did not have the technical means to access and use the data. There were also concerns about methods of data collection, in particular the correct identification of certain land cover and landscape features by API.

Notwithstanding this, there was a great deal of awareness of the potential of GIS to assist in the work of the National Park. Many ideas for possible demonstration projects were put forward and discussed. A common theme was that a great deal of map-based data was being used, but that using paper records hindered efficiency. To address this a project using computer-based mapping was already underway in the drawing office using recently acquired Desk Top Publishing (DTP) systems.

THE EXMOOR GIS DEMONSTRATOR

Following these initial meetings a demonstration project was identified with the objective of monitoring land use change in different types of management area. Of particular interest was the desire to produce a Management Information System (MIS) to assist in the development and monitoring of management plans, and to illustrate how GIS could assist in this process by integrating a variety of land use and related data sets held by the Park while enabling rapid retrieval, analysis and display of these data. The test area chosen for the demonstrator covered the National Park owned land of Larkbarrow and Warren in Exmoor parish, an area of about 10.5 sq. kms.

The demonstrator was developed on the ArcView GIS software (Environmental Systems Research Institute, 1992). ArcView provides a stand-alone Windows-based easy-to-use GIS package, with a point-and-click interface for most functions such as map selection and composition, map overlay, zooming and panning, query of databases and hard copy output. It is extremely flexible in terms of choice of symbolisation for maps and can interface with other Windows software. It should be stressed that it was not the objective of this work to develop a complete working system. Given the limited scope of the project the aim was to illustrate a series of possibilities, to stimulate further discussion of the possible role of GIS within the Park, rather than concentrating on a single application and delivering a finished product.

The main sources of geographical data within Exmoor National Park are currently paper maps and database records (typically where the point location of some attribute such as an archaeological find or a bird nesting site has been recorded using a National Grid reference). Working with geographical information of this type involves a number of potential problems and risks. These include:
* having to work with a series of maps which may be kept in different locations, mapped at different scales and using differing notations;
* knowing exactly what information is available for any particular area;
* drawing overlays which bring together two or more map sources which is difficult and time consuming;
* generating map outputs from traditional database software which is usually difficult and can be impossible;
* having only one copy of key records and maps which limits use;
* wear and tear of paper maps and
* potentially serious difficulties of replacing information if records are lost through accident.

These problems are largely overcome by a move to GIS.

The main achievement of the Exmoor GIS demonstrator is thus to bring together within a single system all the data listed in Table 5. Some data sets were already in computer-compatible form but most were digitised specifically for the purposes of the project. The system allows rapid access to this information through an intuitive simple-to-use point-and-click interface. The information can be manipulated, viewed in various combinations and mapped at a range of scales, regardless of traditional map edges and in conjunction with the Ordnance Survey (OS) digital Land-Line maps at 1:2,500 if so desired.

Data sets used within the Exmoor National Park GIS demonstrator	
Data Set	Source
MLCNP Data	MLCNP Project
Vegetation Survey (1987)	Exmoor National Park
Burning Maps Proposed: 90, 91, 92, 93, 94 Actual: 90, 92, 93	Exmoor National Park
Grazing Livestock Unit Maps	Exmoor National Park
OS 1:2,500 Digital Map Data	Exmoor National Park/ Somerset CC
Birds Survey	Exmoor National Park
Archaeology Database	Exmoor National Park
Aerial Photographs	Exmoor National Park

Table 5 Data sets used within the Exmoor National Park GIS demonstrator.

Figure 28 (colour section) shows an example of the computer interface. Here the user has focused on the Warren management area, has displayed the Proposed 1993 Burn (in red cross-hatching), the Actual 1993 Burn (blue horizontal hatching) and viewed these in conjunction with the Grazing Levels survey (displayed as a choropleth map with the key to the left of the display) and the OS 1:2,500 data.

This display takes a matter of a few seconds to compose, and identifies a number of important patterns, including:

* the correspondence between the proposed and actual burn in 1993;
* exactly where unplanned burns occurred and
* how these patterns relate to the grazing levels survey data.

By using other data sources which are readily available the user could:
* look at the historical record of proposed and actual burns since 1990, in any suitable combination and for any area of interest;
* compare these results with the detailed vegetation survey available, and
* view these records in the context of the MLCNP data for the 1970s and 1980s, together with changes in land cover recorded by the survey.

Moreover as new data are recorded they can be added to the system so that the information content of the system grows and the problem of losing track of what maps and databases are available for an area is avoided.

Figure 29 (colour section) shows another example of using information previously stored within a simple database, namely records of birds' nesting behaviour. Here the user has selected Windchat nesting sites from the 1987 Birds survey (which contains information on a number of species) and has displayed their locations (as black star symbols) in conjunction with the 1980s MLCNP land cover information.

This display allows the user to explore the relationship between the bird sites and land cover. It may be important to explore associations and begin to investigate the development of models to explain bird distributions. For example, if it appears that bird nesting sites favour certain types of landscape this may help in the targeting of survey activities or in the estimation of bird populations. If information on changes in land cover and changes in bird nesting sites are both available more complex analyses of temporal change may be undertaken.

In this brief discussion of the demonstrator the emphasis has been on types of use anticipated from managers and scientists. However the figures used here also raise another general argument in favour of GIS, namely the ability to produce high quality customised cartographic outputs quickly and efficiently. Through the use of GIS, data can be retrieved rapidly, drawn at a range of scales, interactive graphic design and automated drafting tools can be applied and map-based products reproduced quickly. These efficiencies of map production, combined with the opportunities for extracting new information by linking landscape and related environmental data sets, only serve to highlight a key advantage of using GIS, namely data integration and data management.

CONCLUSION

The report of the National Parks Review Panel, *Fit for the Future*, proposed that each Park should produce an environmental inventory, to be updated every five years, which would form the basis for a periodic audit of the environmental assets of the National Park. The MLCNP project and the current work using GIS are important stepping stones to meeting these future information needs for Park monitoring and management.

During the course of the 'Information and Advisory Service' project, Exmoor National Park Authority purchased the MapInfo GIS system (MapInfo Corporation, 1994) and are currently setting up a pilot GIS for managing National Park owned land in the whole of Exmoor parish. Awareness of the potential of GIS, established through the work described here, has led to practical experience of using GIS, the development of 'in-house' expertise and a commitment to GIS from senior management. Whilst still in their infancy, and subject to the availability of resources within the National Park Authority, these are important developments which are ushering in a new era in managing and understanding changes in the landscape of Exmoor.

DISCLAIMER AND ACKNOWLEDGEMENT

The views expressed here are those of the authors and do not necessarily reflect those of the Countryside Commission or any other organisation. The authors acknowledge the assistance of the staff of the Exmoor National Park Authority in the development of the Exmoor GIS demonstrator. The project 'Monitoring Landscape Change in the National Parks: Information and Advisory Service for the Southern Parks' was funded by the Countryside Commission and let as a service contract to the Department of Geography at the University of Bristol.

REFERENCES

Countryside Commission & Countryside Council for Wales, *Landscape Change in the National Parks*, (Manchester, 1991).

DOE, *Countryside Survey 1990 – Main Report*, Countryside 1990 Series 2, (London, 1993).

R. Dunn & A.R. Harrison, *Monitoring Landscape Change in the National Parks: Information and Advisory Service for the Southern Parks*, Final Report to the Countryside Commission, (Cheltenham, 1993).

R. Dunn & A.R. Harrison, *Monitoring Landscape Change in the National Parks: Information and Advisory Service for the Southern Parks* (Phase 2), Final Report to the Countryside Commission, (Cheltenham, 1995).

Environmental Systems Research Institute, *ArcView User's Guide*, (Redlands, California, 1992).

Huntings Technical Services, *Monitoring Landscape Change*, Final Report to the Department of the Environment, (London, 1986).

MapInfo Corporation, *MapInfo Desktop Mapping Software*, (New York, 1994).

Silsoe College, *Landscape Change in the National Parks of England and Wales*, Final Report to the Countryside Commission, (14 vols), (Cheltenham, 1991).

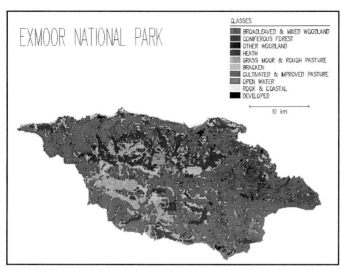

Figure 21 *Distribution of main land cover types in Exmoor National Park (1980).*

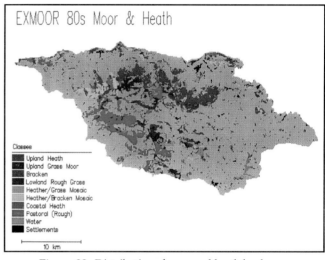

Figure 22 *Distribution of moor and heath land cover types in Exmoor National Park (1980).*

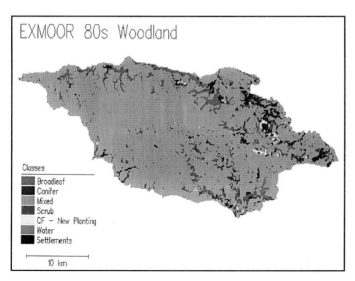

Figure 23 *Distribution of woodland types in Exmoor National Park (1980).*

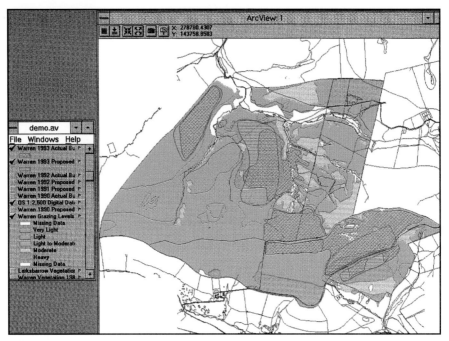

Figure 28 *Warren grazing levels survey together with proposed and actual 1993 burning maps.*

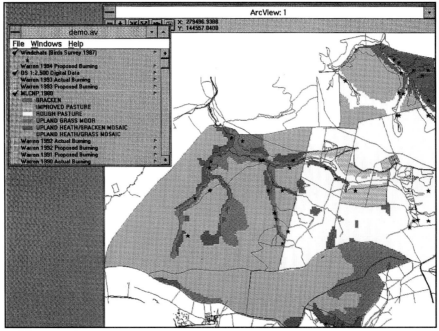

Figure 29 *Location of Windchat nesting sites with MLCNP 1980s land cover data.*

AFTER THE FLOOD: IMAGES OF EXMOOR AS A NATIONAL PARK

Mark Blacksell

Professor of Geographical Sciences, University of Plymouth

In their book, *National Parks: Conservation or Cosmetics?*, still after more than a decade one of the most penetrating analyses of the National Park movement in the UK, Anne and Malcolm MacEwen state bluntly that:

> the title 'National Park' has misled visitors and natives alike for more than 30 years, arousing fears that have little justification and expectations that it has not satisfied. (MacEwen and MacEwen, 1981, 6)

This paper seeks to examine some of those fears and expectations with respect to Exmoor, with a view to determining how well-founded they are, and the extent to which they have changed in the forty years since the National Park was first designated.

The quest is not a new one; there is a veritable avalanche of literature about the UK National Parks, much of it published by the National Park Authorities themselves. In particular, there have been two major reports into the health of National Parks and their way forward that have done much to guide official attitudes (Sandford, 1974; Edwards, 1991). The challenge is to wrest from this mixture of comment and policy those defining images which set Exmoor apart from the wider rural landscape from which it springs.

There is a series of widely acknowledged images associated with Exmoor, some stemming from its cultural history, others from the natural environment and still more from the region's status as a National Park. For me, the great storm that struck on 15 August 1952 is particularly evocative. In the space of less than 24 hours, somewhere in the order of 250 mm of rain fell on The Chains and the higher parts of the western moorland, turning small rivers like the West Lyn into raging torrents and causing extensive landslides (Gifford, 1953). Part of the village of Lynmouth was swept away, along with at least 17 bridges in the surrounding area, while 28 people were drowned, making it one of the worst floods ever recorded in England (Kidson, 1953).

The significance of the storm for the future of Exmoor as a National Park lies in the powerful reminder it provided to the national psyche, just as the programme of National Park designation was getting underway in England and Wales, that nature is never fully tamed and can never be taken for granted. The ensuing floods were a much-needed antidote to the romanticised allure of a rural idyll, which was coming to dominate the prevailing public image of Exmoor (and the other putative National Parks) at the time. It also underscored the inherent fragility of the cultural landscape and the fact that its survival depends on the successful outcome of a battle with the elements, as much as coping with a changing society.

VISIONS FOR EXMOOR

The contemporary view of Exmoor, as set out in the second review of the Exmoor National Park Plan, provides an optimisitic and reassuring vision.

> Whilst ... [Exmoor's] ... 686 sq km (265 sq m) rank it as second smallest of our National Parks (not including the Broads), the sheer variety of its natural beauty, wildlife, history and culture makes it second to none. The high, remote moorland core of Exmoor may have been the primary justification for its National Park designation, but deep combes, with their clear, trout-laden streams and steep wooded sides, the dramatic, often spectacular, coast, the pervading sense of history with legend and lore melting into the reality of past and present cultures, all combine in a magical mixture to make Exmoor what it is.
>
> (Exmoor National Park Authority, 1991, 7)

The key to the future of the landscape is seen to lie in preserving 'the mottled charm' (Porchester, 1977, 18), that derives from the great variety of scenery contained within it.

To sustain this character, ten long-term management aims are spelled out in the plan under the headings landscape, enjoyment, and community:

For the landscape:

1. To conserve and, if possible, extend the existing open moorland and the farm management and grazing practices that underpin it;

2. To care for and maintain the traditional, enclosed, farmed landscapes;

3. To enlarge the area of broad-leaved woodland, and to mitigate the impact of existing conifer plantations;

4. To provide for farming and forestry industries that will support a working population devoted to sustaining the traditional landscape;

5. To strengthen the protection for wildlife and, where possible, encourage the return of 'lost' wildlife populations and species;

6. To compile a complete inventory of, and conservation programme for, Exmoor's natural, historic, archaeological, and cultural resources;

For enjoyment:

7. To encourage less reliance on the motor vehicle generally, reducing vehicular access in the wilder areas; and to enhance the network of public footpaths and bridleways;

8. To improve the quality and extent of the information and interpretation services;

For the community:

9. To promote development policies for the towns and villages, which provide for their social and economic needs, including affordable housing for the local population, but not at the expense of the intrinsic beauty and character of the settlements;

10. To ensure that the people of Exmoor – farmers, foresters, landowners, town and village dwellers, tourism operators, local bodies, organisations and institutions, including the NPA, understand and support each other's interests and are all working together to ensure that Exmoor remains a beautiful place.

All in all, the vision is a firm commitment to preserving Exmoor's life and landscape as a valued part of the national heritage. Fundamental change is to be resisted, so that an area universally considered to be outstandingly beautiful may be conserved for all time.

ACHIEVING A NATIONAL CONSENSUS

The national consensus concerning the beauty of Exmoor and the policies necessary to sustain it has not been achieved easily. It represents the results of a gradual, long-term, change in aesthetic tastes combined with a growing acceptance that the state has a role as conservator in the national interest.

Until the latter part of the eighteenth century, the whole idea of preserving landscape for its own sake, or even as part of the historic record, was an almost complete anathema (Tuan, 1977, 192). The unenclosed moorlands of upland Britain, in particular, were associated with ugliness and fear, without a hint of the grandeur and nostalgia with which they are now invested. Daniel Defoe in one of the letters written during his tour through the island of Great Britain (1724-6) is typically disparaging and dismissive: '...the country it [the River Exe] rises in, is called Exmore, Campden calls it a filthy, barren ground, and, indeed, so it is ...' (Defoe, 1962, 1, 263)

The greater part of what is now the National Park was designated a royal hunting forest and only finally sold into private hands in 1819. The subsequent emphasis was firmly on improvement and enclosure, reclaiming the area for agriculture. The main protagonists in this process were the Knight family, and the story of how they converted the wilderness into agricultural land in the course of the nineteenth century has been memorably researched and told (Orwin and Sellick, 1970). It is a story of enterprise, extreme physical hardship and the constant threat of looming economic disaster; at no stage did landscape preservation form part of the agenda. The Knights, and the other estate owners who controlled the land in what is now the National Park, were concerned with changing the landscape and developing its economic potential.

At the same time the romantic movement, increasingly dominant throughout the nineteenth century, was steadily incorporating the landscape within its purview. The poets, Samuel Taylor Coleridge and William Wordsworth spent time together in the Quantock Hills to the east of Exmoor in the late 1790s while in 1869 R.D. Blackmore published *Lorna Doone*, one of the most successful and widely read of romantic novels, which takes as its theme life on Exmoor on the frontier between wilderness and settled respectability. Gradually, as society became increasingly urbanised and people's lives less directly rooted in the countryside, wilderness and the rural landscape came to be valued for their own sake, rather than just for their capacity to provide a tangible economic return.

The details of the early twentieth century National Park movement in the UK that grew from this general change in national perceptions of the value of rural landscapes, have already been well researched and there is no need to rehearse them again here (MacEwen and MacEwen, 1981 and 1987). Nevertheless, it is relevant to underline the extent of the movement's success and the degree to which attitudes changed. By the time the great social revolution planned for UK society after the end of the Second World War had taken shape, the desirability of measures to preserve the wilder parts of the British countryside was firmly on the agenda and the case for National Parks had already been 'made and won' (Dower, 1945, 6). The outstanding issues were the choice of areas to be designated and how the whole process should be administered. The new National Parks, such as Exmoor, were no longer marginal; they had been recreated with a raft of new purposes added to their traditional agricultural role. Most of the subsequent debate has been about how to devise policies which live up to the enhanced expectations.

PROSPECT AND REALITY

In his seminal report on National Parks in England and Wales John Dower recommended that Exmoor should be part of an early, second instalment of park designations. Though only just falling within his ideal minimum size of 250 sq miles (649.62 sq km), it fulfilled all the requirements of having a relatively wild and beautiful landscape with ample access for open air enjoyment by the public. The recommendation was keenly endorsed by the National Parks Committee (England and Wales), chaired by Sir Arthur Hobhouse, which reported two years later (Hobhouse, 1947). The Hobhouse Committee interpreted the extent of Exmoor very generously, extending the boundary to the south and east 'to take in the beautiful wooded valleys of the Exe, Barle and Haddeo, the little country town of Dulverton, and the whole of the Brendon Hills' (Hobhouse, 1947, 103). The committee also went out of its way to extol the views across the Bristol Channel to the mountains of southern Wales. The most unexpected recommendation,

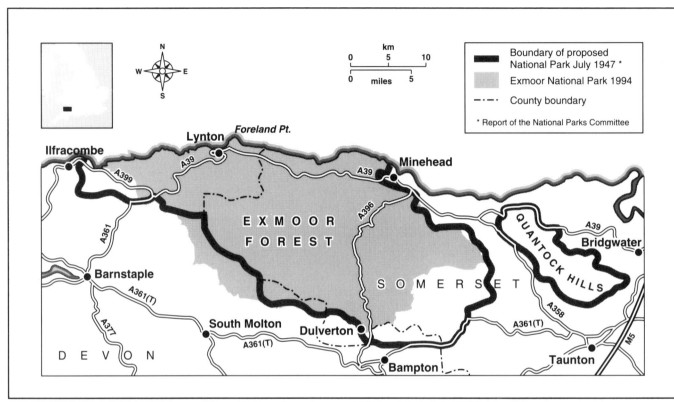

Figure 30 Boundary of proposed National Park, July 1947.

however, was the inclusion of the Quantocks as a separate outlier to the main section of the National Park, referring to them as 'Exmoor in little' (Hobhouse, 1947, 103) (Figure 30).

Taken together, the Dower and Hobhouse reports were a fine combination of vision and practicality, but both failed to predict the future in two important respects. The first misreading related to agriculture, where the scale and impact of mechanisation was crucially underestimated. The future of the rural economy as they saw it is eloquently summed up by Dower:

Given proper care for landscape effect in matters of detail – a care which was taken by eighteenth century improving

landlords as a matter of course – such 'improvement' is in no way inconsistent with the landscape preservation and recreational requirements of a National Park regime. That fuller cultivation should enhance rather than diminish the scenic effect has been strikingly demonstrated by the wartime changes which have turned so many acres of Lake District and Pennine country 'brown side up'. It is above all else to farming, both to extensive grazing of the higher open land and to the more or less intensive grazing, mowing and cropping of the lower, fully enclosed land, that the landscapes of all our potential National Parks owe the manmade element in their character; and it is to the farming communities that we must look for continuance not only of the scenic setting but of the drama itself – the rural life and work, 'the mild continuous epic

98

of the soil', the endless battle between men and nature –
without which the finest of English or Welsh scenery would
lack an essential part of its charm and recreational value.
(Dower, 1945, p. 21)

Even for someone writing in the late 1940s this is a very
romanticised, and sanitized, view of agriculture. The reality is
demonstrated more clearly by Orwin's research into the
nineteenth century reclamation of the Exmoor Forest, which
revealed a brutal assault on the existing open moorland
landscape (Orwin and Sellick, 1970). When reclamation
gathered pace once more in the 1960s and 70s, it quickly
became evident that the traditional heather moorland was once
again being mortally threatened. The confidence in farming as
a benign and protective force of those who had worked so hard
to see Exmoor designated as a National Park was exposed as a
serious miscalculation.

The second failure related to motor vehicles. In common with
nearly everyone else, neither Dower nor Hobhouse foresaw the
explosive growth in their number or how widespread their
ownership would become. An invention viewed as the most
likely medium for realising the potential of National Parks,
was to become a major menace threatening their very survival.
Hobhouse writes with complete equanimity that 'Exmoor is in
fact first rate country for motoring and for walking and riding'
(Hobhouse, 1947, 104). There is not the slightest hint of irony
that of the three forms of locomotion listed, 'motoring' comes
first. In contrast, the current Exmoor National Park Plan states

Plate 33 Visitor enjoyment at Tarr Steps.

that 'National forecasts of vehicular use are alarming. The
combination of greater car ownership and increased leisure
time suggests a potentially significant growth of recreational
journeys to Exmoor, unless either alternative opportunities are
developed away from the National Park or there are severe
economic or other constraints on vehicular use' (Exmoor
National Park Authority, 1991, 76).

It is also worth remembering, that in making the case for its
proposed National Park designations, the Hobhouse
Committee made a positive virtue of their proximity to large
centres of population, in some cases with hilarious results.
Appendix D of the report, for instance, reveals that three of the
four cities closest to Exmoor are Cardiff, Swansea and the
Rhondda! Although a footnote explains that this is based on
the distances measured directly over the Bristol Channel, it
nevertheless gives the impression of a somewhat spurious, and
superfluous, exercise (Hobhouse, 1947, 124). Today, attitudes
have changed totally. Accessibility is taken for granted and the
concern is that too many people will descend on the National
Park, not too few.

MANAGING CHANGE

Under the terms of the National Parks and Access to the
Countryside Act (1949), Exmoor, not including the Quantocks,
became a National Park on 19 October 1954. It did so, however,
in the face of determined opposition from both Devon and
Somerset County Councils, the local authorities charged jointly
with administering it. Although, in landscape terms, the
boundaries were arbitrary and controversial, they have
nevertheless provided the framework within which the Park
has evolved its present identity. The most widely read book
about Exmoor was rewritten to take account of the new reality
of the National Park (Burton, 1969) and an official government
guide was published on behalf of the Countryside Commission
(Coleman-Cooke, 1970). In 1958 the Exmoor Society was
formed by a group of interested and committed individuals
and immediately began to campaign on behalf of Exmoor, not
least through the Exmoor Review, first published in 1959, and a
host of other defining publications.

The least active and effective agent in the first two decades of the National Park's existence was the National Park Committee. Split administratively between two County Councils, both of which had opposed the designation of Exmoor as a National Park, it suffered, not surprisingly, from a permanent paralysis, which rendered it incapable of influencing either the direction or the pace of development. The central conflict on Exmoor was the ploughing and fencing of open moorland, but despite lip-service being paid to cooperation with the farming community over the issue by agreeing a Critical Amenity Area in 1968, little real control was achieved. Other National Park Committees were similarly lacking in dynamism and, by the end of the 1960s, the whole National Park programme was dogged by a pervasive sense of drift. In an attempt to break the depressing deadlock, the Secretary of State for the Environment appointed a National Parks Policies Review Committee, under the chairmanship of Lord Sandford, in 1972, to review the whole future of the National Park system.

With the benefit of hindsight, the subsequent report appears surprisingly sympathetic to the lack of activity by National Park Boards and Committees. It commends them for their efforts, but accepts that they had been hamstrung by inadequate powers and in some cases, including Exmoor, by an unworkable administrative structure (Sandford, 1974). Although the committee made a number of recommendations about the balance of priorities in National Park policies between landscape conservation, recreation, and the needs of local communities, it is now clear that it really pinned its hopes for a brighter future on administrative reform.

The Local Government Act (1972) provided the key, paving the way for the present system, whereby each National Park Committee, or Board, has to appoint a National Park Officer and supporting staff, with 80% of the funding coming from central government. The first task of the new authorities, for that in effect is what they became, was to produce a National Park Plan, which had to be approved by the Countryside Commission on behalf of the government.

The new system proved a watershed in all the National Parks,

though was by no means an immediate panacea. Appointing the National Park Officers and establishing the authorities proved very difficult, because they incorporated a completely new set of ideas, which had to be realised by different bodies across the country. Any central guidance was severely circumscribed by the dictates of local government independence.

As far as Exmoor was concerned, however, matters were brought to a head for the new committee by the perennial problem of moorland conversion. Conflict over this issue became so acrimonious and intense that in 1977 the Secretary of State for the Environment and the Minister of Agriculture jointly asked Lord Porchester to undertake an inquiry to establish the true extent of moorland conversion and to advise them on the action they should take. The ensuing report confirmed the problem and recommended that the National Park Authority produce definitive maps of moorland and be provided with the financial means to compensate farmers prevented from converting moorland for income foregone (Porchester, 1977).

The details of the scheme agreed have been thoroughly analysed and discussed elsewhere (MacEwen and MacEwen, 1987, 135-42), but for Exmoor it assumed an importance extending well beyond the immediate issue of moorland conversion. The introduction of the scheme forced a warring and riven committee, that manifestly lacked any coherent and agreed strategy, to face up to its responsibilities as a National Park Authority and to begin working together to promote the interests of Exmoor as a National Park. That is not to say that differences of view and priority were banished, but for the first time there did emerge a consensus, that the landscape of Exmoor within the National Park boundaries was more than just another administrative subdivision and that its future could not be measured against the same criteria as the rest of the rural landscape.

All the ten National Parks in England and Wales suffered to some extent from the kind of identity crisis that afflicted Exmoor, although the details in each case were different, and nowhere else was the level of disagreement so intense. More than anything else, it was this uncertainty about the direction of policy that led to the charges, levelled by the MacEwens and referred to at the outset, of misrepresentation and false expectations (MacEwen and MacEwen, 1981, 6).

Looking back, it is astonishing how distant that unhappy memory now seems. The future for National Parks may still fall short of the ideals cherished by Dower, but they are now unquestionably secure; their landscape widely accepted as part of the national heritage and therefore deserving of special protection by the government. The credit for the changes of attitude must be given to the leadership provided, not just by the new National Park committees, but also by a succession of National Park Officers, backed up by their professional staffs. These men and women have gained the trust and respect of the committees they serve, identifying with the National Parks they represent and, in the process, creating new, and more coherent landscapes out of the areas that were designated some four decades ago.

FIT FOR THE FUTURE?

In 1991 a second review of National Parks in England and Wales was published, in this instance sponsored jointly by the Countryside Commission for England and the Countryside Council for Wales, rather than by the government directly. Nevertheless, it is fascinating to compare the findings with those of its predecessor (Edwards, 1991; Sandford, 1974). The list of recommendations is extensive, covering every aspect of life and work in National Parks, but ultimately, once again, heavy reliance for future progress is placed on administrative reform. The report urges the government to draw up and enact a new National Parks Act, the central measure of which would be the creation of fully independent authorities with the formal title of National Park Authority.

The case advanced for the change is that, although National Parks have achieved much greater independence since the Local Government Act (1972) was enacted in 1974, their development is still overly influenced by local, and often conflicting , considerations, rather than national ones.

It is an argument that has ebbed and flowed ever since the Parks were designated and, initially, the government showed little real sign of being convinced of the need for the radical change for which the Edwards' report argued. After waiting more than two years, an alliance of pressure groups persuaded Lord Norrie to introduce a National Parks Bill into the House of Lords on his own behalf, but it did not attract government support and eventually failed in the House of Commons. In November 1994, however, the government included, as part of a new Environment Bill (1994/5 HL Bill 10), provision for a change in the administrative status of National Parks in England and Wales. Part III of the Bill provides for independent National Park Authorities, responsible for all planning matters, from April 1996. Two third of the members will be appointed by the local authorities with an interest in the area covered by each National Park. On Exmoor this would be Devon and Somerset County Councils and North Devon and West Somerset District Councils, with the District Councils having the option of nominating up to a third of the membership. The other third of members would be nominated nationally by the Secretary of State for the Environment, as at present. The new National Park Authorities will continue to receive at least 75% of their funds from central government, and will have the power to precept the remaining 25% directly from the nominating local authorities, a system that has worked well in the Peak District and the Lake District since those National Parks were first created in the 1950s. The other changes proposed in the Bill are relatively minor. There is a strengthening of the regard that National Park Authorities must have for the social and economic well-being of local communities, and government authorities have to have regard for National Park purposes when their activities impinge on these officially protected areas.

It remains to be seen whether a change of administrative status into independent National Park Authorities, less closely tied to local government, will be sufficient to secure the ambitious vision that the review committee set out for National Parks into the next century (Edwards, 1991). The report sees the future for the National Parks in England and Wales, increasingly, as refuges of international importance from the ravages that threaten so much of the global environment. Returning (albeit very obliquely!) to my initial theme of the flood, the Edwards committee believes that places like Exmoor today have a similar importance to the ark when the world was inundated in the time of Noah. It is an awesome responsibility for those charged with administering National Parks, and a considerably greater one than was envisaged by even the most farsighted of the people who worked so tirelessly to establish the system in the first half of this century.

REFERENCES

S.H.Burton, *Exmoor* , (1969).

J. Coleman-Cooke, ed. *Exmoor National Park Guide No. 8*, (1970).

D. Defoe, *A Tour Through the Whole of the Island of Great Britain*, 2 vols., (1962).

J. Dower, *National Parks in England and Wales*, (1945).

R. Edwards, *Fit for the Future*. Report of the National Parks Review Panel, (Cheltenham, 1991).

Exmoor National Park Authority, *Exmoor National Park Plan 1991-1996*, (Dulverton, 1991).

J. Gifford, 'Landslides on Exmoor caused by the storm of 15 August 1952', *Geography* 179(1), (1953) 9-17.

A. Hobhouse, *Report of the National Parks Committee (England and Wales)*, (1947).

C. Kidson, 'The Exmoor storm and the Lynmouth floods', *Geography* 179 (1), (1953) 1-9.

A. and M. MacEwen, *National Parks: Conservation or Cosmetics?* (1981).

A. and M. MacEwen, *Greenprints for the Countryside? The Story of Britain's National Parks*, (1987).

C.S. Orwin and R.J. Sellick, *The Reclamation of Exmoor Forest*, (Newton Abbot, 1970).

Lord Porchester, *A Study of Exmoor*, (1977).

Lord Sandford, *Report of National Parks Policies Review Committee*, (1974).

Y. Tuan, *Space and Place. The Perspective of Experience*, (1977).

POSTCRIPT:
EXMOOR'S FUTURE AS A NATIONAL PARK

Rachel Thomas

Countryside Commissioner
and sometime Member of the Exmoor National Park Committee

Celebrating Exmoor's Fortieth Anniversary as a National Park gives an opportunity to reflect quietly on the reasons for its creation and continuation. Why as a nation have we drawn complicated and well fought over lines around certain areas, called them National Parks and given them separate legislation, administration and finance? In a more environmentally sensitive age with greater green awareness and action is it necessary any more to defend such lines? All of the countryside needs protection and management and it may appear rather naive and elitist to select out a few parts, just 10% of the land surface of England and Wales, and to employ over 1,000 people to look after their conservation and recreation interests. There needs to be a conviction that there are special qualities and purposes about such places that they should be so maintained.

It is the wilderness concept that provides the driving force for considering these areas as special, a quality understood by the early founders, but rather lost and faded since. Consider the extensions of the work of the National Park Authorities from strategic planning to development control; from functional strategies to NPSG and now PES; from notification procedures for farming and forestry to farm conservation schemes and management agreements; from the provision of visitor facilities to guided walks and environmental education; and from community support to affordable housing and the marketing of goods. The list is endless. All this has shifted the focus and

has been reinforced by a tourist industry promoting soft images of beautiful places, peacefulness, a sense of the past 'where time moves slowly' and heritage experiences and nostalgia. But look at the other side: extensive tracts of semi-natural vegetation providing rare habitats for wildlife to flourish; large spaces of awesome open country giving a perceived feeling of wildness and opportunities for solitude and reflection; harsh challenges for young people, and old, under rapidly changing weather conditions, presenting a contrast to the softness of urban living; a local community with a long tradition of working a difficult soil for a meagre living and proud of the slow continuity and sudden changes and the interaction of wildlife, people and the land. These are the real images presenting a vitality and dynamism so often missing from the picture and directing the attention to the wildness and people's inter-relationship with the natural world.

At the heart then of the concept of National Parks is the protection of areas that are large in extent, semi-open in landscape, semi-natural in vegetation and with a perceived feeling of wildness and remoteness, giving opportunities for open air recreation.

Started by the 1949 Act they covered, in the words of the Dower Report, 'extensive areas of beautiful and relatively wild country'. Exmoor came into being forty years ago with the glowing words of Hobhouse, 'Here is a potential National Park which is happily free from serious problems'. Indeed, with its 'hogs-back' coastline plunging fearlessly into the Bristol Channel and its extensive tracts of moorland ridges receding into far distances, and fierce combes dissecting the upland plateau and semi-natural woodland clothing much of the moorland rim, it fitted the description well. Although one of the smallest National Parks (pocket sized compared with its larger colleagues to the north), it provided an intermixture of moorland, farmland, woodland and coast giving a marvellous mosaic of contrasts with the large areas of moorland, rare in Southern England, dominating the whole.

The Edwards Review Panel, set up by the Countryside Commission to look at the future of National Parks, endorsed in 1991 their essential ingredients. 'The National Parks still contain the greatest tracts of open countryside, the strongest sense of remoteness and the greatest and most dramatic scenery where nature seems to be most about us' ... and further on the Report states, 'if an area is to merit the title National Park these qualities must be combined over extensive tracts of distinctive countryside which provide a sense of wildness'.

Here then is the challenge for Exmoor as a National Park. Does it have sufficient tracts of moorland or are the blocks now too fragmented? Does it have woodlands that are extensive in scale or truly numerous, or are they too confined to the northern slopes of the Brendon Hills and the coastal cliffs and some valley sides? Is the coast undeveloped or are the tentacles of settlement spreading outwards? Is the farmed landscape in good heart? Is there a sufficient experience of wildness and remoteness and the opportunities for physical challenge? Alternatively, is the moor too tamed, with on-site information boards, signposts, waymarked walks and car-park provision? It is these broad brush questions that must be asked and kept in mind when looking at the future of National Parks. Otherwise the justification for retaining them, with their intensity of management and public spending, will wither away since other areas of the countryside also have pressing needs. In our small, crowded and long-settled island, National Parks provide contrasts to a tamed countryside and urban and suburbanised living and give the opportunity for physical challenge and spiritual refreshment.

Opportunities for guiding landscape change on Exmoor are at their greatest now with radical changes in agriculture and land use. The tools are there to be used imaginatively, with financial incentives more available and sophisticated techniques of environmental management being practised. Exmoor's Section 3 Conservation Map identifies clearly the wilder areas to be retained and provides a data base on which to build a comprehensive landscape strategy for the future.

The proportion of open country stands at 23%, which is small when compared with other National Parks. By working with the natural grain of the land, potentially wild areas can be established by selecting criteria based on both nature and landscape requirements. For nature, a better ecological balance has to be recognised and the needs of wildlife have to play a greater part in establishing priorities. For landscape, aesthetic qualities of scale, openness, remoteness and contrasts can be included, and archaeological remains such as round barrows and Roman forts can be placed again in wilder settings. For recreation, woodland landscapes that can absorb people and different kinds of activity can be extended. Not all the landscape features nor intrusive infrastructure need to be retained. In some places, hedges can be left to disappear into the moorland and some buildings and roads left to decay. Opportunities through traffic measures to provide the 'long walk in' can be found. And perhaps the impact of the nineteenth century restoration of Exmoor Forest can be reduced. Dare I suggest the plug being pulled out at Pinkworthy Pond or the Knight's boundary wall being forgotten? For forests, restructuring through sensitive forest design is now a possibility and there is the potential to extend the native woodlands. For management of wild country must not freeze landscapes at some point in time: history must continue with new landscapes and habitats created for new lifestyles in the twenty-first century. Tomorrow's Exmoor will be a different place.

Gavin Maxwell wrote 'I am convinced that man has suffered from his separation from the soil and from other living creatures of the world, the evolution of his intellect has outrun his needs as an individual, and as yet he must still, for security, look long and hard at some portion of the earth as it was before he tampered with it!' Exmoor is a place for 'looking long and hard' for it still retains a feeling of wildness and remoteness even though the reality of not being tampered with is illusory. Walk down Hoar Oak Water from the Exe watershed into a lost valley of long slopes, or look out at dusk from Limecombe to the long moorland ridge line mysteriously broken by the series of round barrows, or pass through the Barle woodlands with their dark vegetation against the water, and the illusion is complete. Exmoor and wildness, not wilderness but chance pleasure; that is its future as a National Park.

(Courtesy Brian Pearce).